BECOMING A POSTPARTUM DOULA

Wisdom, Tips, and Guidance for Your Journey

Betsy K. Schwartz

Birth in the Know, LLC

Imprint: Independently published

ISBN-13: 9798791385376

Printed in the United States of America

This book is dedicated to all the doulas who support new and expectant families. And, to all those who are considering this heart-centered calling.

CONTENTS

PREFACE

My goal with this book is to inspire you, excite you, and cause you to take the next step that works for you in fulfilling your dream of being a postpartum doula, starting your business, and living the life you want.

If you're looking for an academic book with a huge bibliography, this is not it. This book is me talking to you as if we're in an in-person conversation or on the phone. It includes practical tools and tips you can use and apply immediately. Take what you like, and leave the rest. Be open to receive exactly what you need.

Before diving in, I want to share a little bit about my own journey, so you can better understand how I was called to this work.

Growing up, I loved the outdoors: running in the woods, playing in the swamp, climbing trees, playing softball and kickball. This is what I was born to do; to play and have fun. All the neighborhood kids used to explore and have fun together.

Secretly, I always wanted to be a boy because it seemed that they had more privileges and were treated differently. Boys got to do all the fun sports like hockey. Boys got to wear pants to school. It wasn't fair at all.

I was a bit jealous of my older brother, though I loved to get his clothes when they got too small for him. You can imagine how excited I was when girls were allowed to wear pants to school. I was the first one to put on those pants.

When I turned 13, I got my period. My dream of becoming a boy was over. I had to face the fact that I was (and always would be) a girl, and would grow up to be a woman. I had heard about this feminine curse, and was not happy that it had happened to me.

I wasn't one of those girls who longed for marriage and babies -- far from it. It's funny to think back to that time now. It wasn't until I became a mother for the first time, in 1989, that I felt like I found home -- something I was good at and more than enjoyed.

Being a mother made me feel worthy, and connected. I surprised myself at how much I knew intuitively, and I had no idea how I knew. It was as if being a mothers was what I was meant to do. I never knew how much love I could feel for another person. This entrance into the hood (motherhood), is what led me into becoming a postpartum doula, and eventually a trainer.

Giving birth and raising two boys was the hardest and best, most rewarding experience of my life. Many moments of growth, insanity, depression, joy, angst, shame, guilt, and fun. But if you told me in my early childhood, that I would be a postpartum doula and trainer, I would have told you, "You're nuts." Babies and marriage were the furthest things from my mind.

Instead, I dreamed of other things. I knew I was destined to learn, to become the wisest person I could be. Nana Sally, my favorite grandmother, always had something wise to say. And, she was a great cook. I loved the smell of Nana's kitchen, and dreamed of being a great cook, maybe even a caterer like my Nana. Aside from learning a lot about cooking, one of the biggest lessons I got from Nana was that nobody could take away your education.

I wanted to make a difference in the world doing something I loved. At the age of 13, even though I didn't have it all figured out, I knew that the world needed some help. My own curious nature would lead me to explore and take risks, to learn about life and to experience many different people, places and things.

Eventually, I discovered the world of maternal care. But in the 1970s and early 1980s, postpartum doulas were not well-known. It wasn't until the 1970s when the words *doula* and *matresence* were coined. You'll read about that later on.

Learning that I could be paid for something I loved to do -- that was so rewarding to me -- was like winning the lottery. Mothering new mothers became my "job." This is what postpartum doulas do.

Through experience working with many women, I have learned that not every new mother experiences the instantaneous, unconditional love for their newborn. Some mothers are comfortable and confident with caring for their baby, while others are anxious and uncertain.

The first time I was pregnant, I felt I didn't know anything. I was afraid and anxious. My now deceased ex-husband deserted us when I was seven months pregnant. It was a painful time in my life. However, I discovered I possessed an internal guidance system -- a knowing from somewhere -- and was somehow able to tap into this guidance when my son was born.

Being a mother challenges a woman in so many ways, no matter what the circumstances of her life are at the time. It causes her to dig deep into her soul, to surrender to the task of raising a tiny human. I was not enlightened when I became pregnant the first time. The term *Conscious Parenting* was not on my radar. Being mindful, conscious and present takes practice. It wasn't until my boys were almost grown that I learned about meditation and Reiki, and began a yoga practice.

I'm not sure anybody is really ready for the job of mother. We do the best we can with what we know. Passing on the knowledge and lessons is where the growth accelerates. Providing support during this transitional and transformational time is a blessing.

This poem was written at the third meeting of the Coalition for Improving Maternity Services. I feel it sums up what doulas and other birth workers are all about.

On CIMS '98

A meeting of the minds
Hearts and Souls united
Bonded by a higher mission

Driven by passion.

Passion for women
Passion for children
Passion for families

Changing the culture of birth
TOGETHER
Growing, evolving, teaching, reaching…
For the moon, the stars, the universe.

Endless possibilities
Becoming realities
Bonded by a higher mission
Driven by passion.

Chapter 1 - Combining Old School With Modern Ways

Later on you're going to read about the balance between setting measurable goals, and setting intentions. It's like balancing the Yin and the Yang, the masculine and the feminine energies that reside within each of us. I consider myself "old school," meaning I am of the time before technology, and the breaking of the barriers of communication and information. Thus I write and speak from that perspective. Yet, I also recognize that the world I grew up in, and started my business in, has become antiquated and outdated in many ways.

While many old ways are still relevant -- talking in person or on the phone, and visually being connected with people -- energetically we can connect with people near and far. With the technology we have, there is potential to reach and serve many more clients. I recognize that the generations that came after me (maybe you) have been brought up with the technology, and their children will likely never know a world where the phone was hung on the wall, or how there were only 4 TV channels (all black and white). Maybe this is you.

How can you use this technology and still incorporate the older wisdom? Or how can you use the old ways, and incorporate the technology? This comes down to a willingness to learn, and to step out of your comfort zone.

Being a doula is a heart-centered calling, and earning an honest living from it is absolutely essential for success, joy and freedom. Social media platforms are a great way to expand reach, and market to your target audience. What is most important is maintaining integrity and honesty in all the marketing you do. It's very easy to look a certain way online, and be another way in person. Be true to yourself in all your endeavors.

While you may believe that talking on the phone takes too much time, it also may be the one thing that seals the deal with your client. You can use it as you see fit, especially in cases where your potential client or customer tells you the phone is their preferred way to communicate. With so many options, why not find out how *they* best communicate -- and also let them know what works best for you?

Communication is key to your success. Research tells us that most communication occurs through body language and tone. If you aren't in front of someone, how can you have the best possible exchange of needs? How can you communicate clearly about who you are and how you can best support them?

This is a great question. It's for you to answer. There are courses on communication, social media, and anything else you can imagine. You'll know what feels right and best for you and your clients. I believe expanding your view, and being willing to utilize tools from both the "old school" and the modern way makes the most sense.

While you are in the process of deciding whether being a postpartum doula is right for you, you can try on different ways of communicating. Ask questions in doula groups on social media, call someone who knows more than you do, talk to younger doulas, and older doulas. Information overload is always possible -- but gathering a great amount of wisdom from a variety of sources will then allow you to decipher what you want to use.

I'll always invite and encourage you to trust your inner guidance system. All the information in the world can't help *you* make up *your* mind to do something (or not). This is an inside job. If you find something uncomfortable, perhaps it's an opportunity for growth -- or it could be something you are supposed to avoid. Nobody can figure that out for you, it simply takes practice tuning into what feels right for you.

Making a choice to be a postpartum doula is different now than it was for me. Doulas are more well-known, yet also not recognized everywhere. The explosion of social media has created a world where everyone can voice their message, and be seen. Yet, it's still about truly connecting with the people you want to serve.

Age doesn't matter necessarily, but your lived experience is what you know. You will bring your perspective, beliefs and conditioning with you. Meeting people where they are is what will allow you to provide the support that's needed -- no matter if you are of the "old school," or are a modern day social media maven?

Your clients will have a different lived experience than you. If you find that you can easily attract them to your business and services, and you then connect with them in such a way as to cause them to hire you -- awesome. Many new doulas struggle to seal the deal. There are two components to this. There is the messaging and then there is the human connection.

Doula training and classes vary widely because each trainer brings something unique to the table. This happens even within the same training organization. The classes won't teach you exactly "how to" get clients. There will be strategies presented, and things that others have done -- but at the end of the day, you get to show up as the unique person you are and get your contract signed.

I recommend you keep an open mind as to what methods you use in your marketing, and how you attract the clients you want to serve. Mix it up, and try something that feels uncomfortable. Develop habits that keep you in the game and propel you forward.

If you are still in the "thinking about" being a doula stage, use the parts of this book that make sense to you. Is being a doula what your heart truly desires right now? Do you think you have what it takes to learn what you can, and to be of service to women and families?

Once you say yes, believe that all the right people and circumstances will come to you for assistance - giving you exactly what you need to make it all happen.

Chapter 2 - Why, What And How

The Inside Journey is Where to Begin

With any new adventure (or even something you have been doing for a while), this is the first question to ask yourself: *Why* do you want to do this? Start writing about it. See what comes up for you. There are many reasons why you want to do certain things. If you're reading this book, being a postpartum doula is something you are considering. Or maybe you are already a postpartum doula, but you're not exactly where you thought you'd be with your business. When you're struggling to figure stuff out, you can always come back to your *Why*.

Your *Why* will drive you, and keep you in the game. Being a postpartum doula is more than a job or a career. When I was doing a lot of live weekend workshops for postpartum doulas, I could pick out the few that I knew would go all the way. Meaning, they would follow through with the whole certification program. That doesn't necessarily mean they were the best postpartum doulas -- but they showed up to every class with their passion, excitement and determination.

Taking a class doesn't make you a postpartum doula. You either are one or you aren't. It's a heart-centered calling. So many doulas come to this work because of their own experience. They want to support other women, so they don't have to go through what they went through. It is a way of giving back, or paying it forward. The only thing I would say to that is to be aware of your experience, and think about whether you're attempting to heal yourself through this work -- or if you've done the work to heal, and now want to ignite healing in others.

Why do you want to be the emotional, physical, and practical support for a new mother and her family? Why does this speak to your soul?

For me, it was in the search for purpose and meaning in my life. I needed to work because I was a single mother, and the sole earner. When I was married and seven months pregnant, my now deceased ex-husband deserted us. He was an addict and needed help. This time in my life was one of major transformation. With support and determination, I was able to support myself and my son.

I had fallen in love with being a mother, which was never a dream of mine as it is for so many. When my son Matthew was about two years old, I saw an ad to help other mothers after birth. This spoke to me. To do what my own mother had done for me (knowing how that made me feel), and to get paid to do it seemed like a fantasy. Yet, there it was in black and white in the Help Wanted section of a local paper in Boston.

What and How?

Once you know why you want to be a postpartum doula, you can then ask yourself what you want. This could be a certain amount of clients per year, or it could be to wake up every day excited about going to work. Maybe it is the freedom to create your own schedule.

Beyond those things, what do you really want for your life? Most people want to feel happy and free. Are you thinking that being a postpartum doula will do that for you? I'm going to tell you that it won't. But wait -- didn't I just tell you how I had been searching for meaning and purpose, and bingo, I found a job that gave me that?

Happiness and freedom are both inside jobs. When you seek to create this outside of yourself, you are then attaching your happiness and freedom to that thing. Being happy and free depends on your mindset, perspective and approach to life. As I've grown spiritually, my perspective has changed because of what I've experienced since the beginning of my career.

Being a postpartum doula is an extension of you expressing your love and your desire to connect and nurture another human being during a profound, life-changing event. You're not "giving to receive." Yet, you do receive so many rewards -- including monetary compensation.

Let's say your big Why is to make money doing something you love. That's awesome. Everyone wants to work, make money and love what they're doing in the process. However, if money is the number one goal, you may be setting yourself up for disappointment. The money won't buy you the happiness and the freedom. It will add to those, for sure.

Everything begins within, as I discovered more fully in a personal transformational program. Taking a deep dive within allowed me to learn many things about myself, and how to see things from different perspectives. One great lesson was be, do, and have.

Start with your way of being, then start doing and then you'll have. What do I mean by your way of being? Are you being thoughtful, angry, frustrated, righteous, or joyful? When you check in with yourself on how you're being, you will likely figure out what to do or not to do. For example, if you're feeling frustrated about what someone else is doing, ask yourself "Why am I so frustrated?"

What is it about what the other person is doing that is causing you to be frustrated? It has nothing to do with them, and everything to do with you. When you're a postpartum doula you will witness many choices that others make, and it may not be the choice you make. You may feel frustrated at times because you think, If they made a different choice it would be so much better. Maybe or maybe not.

You get to step back, and notice how you're being before you say or do anything. Coming from a place of love, compassion and understanding will create a very different response.

This inner work is ongoing. There's no one and done. You'll be reflecting and choosing next steps based on what's working and what isn't. The more you know about yourself, and what inspires you and propels you forward, the more likely you are to succeed with the goals you create.

How Am I Going to Do Any of This?

This is where most people (including myself) get stuck. We want something so badly, we have taken the classes, gotten the support from family and friends, and we have all the goals and intentions written out.

Now what?

Many people have said that once you make a commitment and start taking action, all the "how-tos" will be revealed in time. It does help to have an end goal in mind and then create some action items to get you there.

If you get stuck on how, you can do several things. Ask others that have already done it, read and research, practice positive self-talk, or step back and take a break. There is no right or wrong, or any one way to accomplish your goals. You'll never be done. You'll go through this process over and over. Once you've reached a milestone, there will be another one to reach.

I might add that goal setting is the western way. Linear thinking is often associated with male energy, and is definitely needed. Setting intentions and visualizing, which I mentioned previously, is becoming more widespread. For me, a combination of the two works well. You can't just sit around and meditate and visualize your way to success.

You can utilize this practice to stay focused and grounded in your commitment to yourself, and to open yourself up to conspire with the universe.

This might sound airy fairy, but I believe that energy is all there is. In its purest form, it is love. That's why your way of being matters. That's the energy that will create what's next. Think about making choices and taking action when you're angry vs. making choices and taking action when you're calm. The difference is huge -- like night and day, black and white.

Decide what you want, and go for it, no matter what. If I had listened to the naysayers or even my own self-doubt, I never would have started the first postpartum doula service in South Florida. I never would have created, manufactured and marketed Down the Canal – the Game of Birth. I probably never would have gotten married and given birth twice. Or written this book.

When we're trying to figure out *how*, the decision to do something might never happen. We can't know how to do something we've never done before. Even if you get advice from someone else, or they tell you how they did it, it may not be how you would approach it.

I think it's easier to get caught up in the not-knowing rather than embracing the fact that even if we don't know, it can still be done. You can and you will figure it out, if you want it bad enough.

Here are some stories from other long-time doulas. Find out about their big why, and lots of lessons learned as you read on. Let these stories inspire you. Everyone comes to this work from a different path. Many doulas realize that their experience can help someone else. Perhaps they had no support, a traumatic birth, or a perinatal mood disorder. Our own life experience gives us wisdom and empathy we can share with others.

Chapter 3 - Longtime Doula's Stories

Crystal Sada

Crystal Sada has been an advocate for birthing families for 44 years. She has been a certified childbirth educator for 38 years and was a labor and postpartum doula for 16 years. Currently she teaches labor and postpartum doulas and is a LCCE with Lamaze. Crystal and her husband Jerry reside in NJ and are the parents of three adult children and grandparents to seven. **https://www.activebirthinstitute.com/**

"Over my several decades of working with new families, many have asked why I became a postpartum doula. My background includes having worked in maternity as a CNA where my primary responsibility was educating new parents in how to feed and care for their babies. Each night I would go from room to room asking if there was anything I could help them learn or if they had any questions. Back then, we kept mothers and babies for 5-7 days. So, there was plenty of time for teaching and learning. My supervisor was hearing really positive feedback about my teaching and asked if I would like to become a childbirth educator. She sent me to a workshop, and as a result, I have been teaching since 1982.

But for me the biggest factor was the birth of our first daughter in 1976. I had no help whatsoever except from my 17-year-old brother and my husband. When I reflect back, I realize what a difficult time it was, which more than likely led to my failure to breastfeed her beyond two weeks.

She was also taken from me at birth and kept in a special care nursery for 24 hours for no other reason than she was born by cesarean. I didn't get to see her until the next day. Not even a peek. Visitors were coming and telling me what my baby looked like and it had a huge impact. At the time I didn't know any better and being somewhat of a rule follower, I didn't even question it.

About 27 years ago I was very dissatisfied with my full-time job and was looking for something else to do with my life. Someone close to me suggested I do what I was so very good at, working with new families and babies. And that is when it began. I founded Helping Hands Doula Service and tagged that with "Helping families form loving bonds."

My business took off and for 16 years, I worked with hundreds of families providing postpartum care. I also began training postpartum doulas in 2000.

Patience has not always been my strong suit. As a labor support doula, I had to learn really quickly that I needed to be patient! And I did. I could be the quietest and most patient person in the room and most times I was. Others drew off of that. I had to roll that over into my postpartum work as well.

New parents need someone calm and patient. If not, they tend to internalize that as they are not good enough. A prime example of this was a couple who wanted to bathe their newborn themselves. But they wanted me standing nearby to guide them. I agreed. We gathered all the supplies needed and had everything ready for a sponge bath.

It literally took them one full hour to accomplish the bath and dressing of the baby. There were times I felt like flying out of my skin, thinking I could have had it done in five minutes. I kept reminding myself that of course I could, I had worked in a newborn nursery!

About two years later the mother called me. She laughed about how long it took and how patient and understanding I was with them moving like turtles, and their constant worry they were hurting the baby. She reminded me that I never once judged them or tried to rush them. For me, it drove home that we really do need to be patient and allow clients to grow and learn. And they will!

I have also learned that this is really what I am good at. I am good with new families and I am good with babies, and I am no longer one bit concerned with verbalizing that.

As for business, I wish I could go back and have a do-over. Don't we all? I did some things really, really well, and other things not so well. We all know the motto – "If I knew then what I know now" – and I agree with that 100%. Nothing big, just some of the little things. Like when my husband became ill, instead of giving up and panicking about money and health insurance -- trying to figure out what was out there that could help with those two major stresses. Because typically, where there is a will, there is a way.

Don't be afraid to put yourself out there. You need to go out into the community and promote yourself. No one is going to come to you. Start with a nice logo. Something that makes sense and is inclusive. Put together a simple business card. One that is not too busy. Learn to make brochures on Word. It is easy. They can be costly and often people throw them away anyway. Words matter, but fancy doesn't.

Go to doctors, midwives, massage therapists, chiropractors and talk with them about what you do, and how you can help their patients. Let them know that a postpartum doula does not give medical advice. They help the new family adjust, which in turn makes their jobs easier. Don't worry about bragging about how good you are and how well trained you are. Just say it… and MEAN it! Become good, really good. Then let everyone know how good you are.

But most of all, get out there in person -- the good old fashioned way. Social media is great, but goes just so far. Meeting in person always seals the deal. Ask if you can bring bagels and coffee, and give a small presentation to their office. Don't overstay your welcome! And bring brochures, a plastic brochure holder and business cards. Keep them in the trunk of your car so you are ready. You never know who will want them for their office.

Pay unemployment and social security tax. I didn't think about social security, but I sure do now. Back when I did this, social security was optional. I opted not to pay into it and I am very sorry now. Make sure your tax person is great and taking good care of you while also following the laws.

The joys of this work are numerous. Watching new parents bond and become a family. Walking up to a home, and having a new parent throw open the door with tears rolling down their face because the doula has arrived! Remember, they are feeling so isolated and lonely and now there is another adult human being.

Working in the kitchen, loading the dishwasher, and hearing a parent who has had little sleep snoring on the sofa while you quietly work -- it helps you know everything is going to be okay.

Some challenges for me in this work have been seeing how poorly some families get along. Family dynamics are complicated and not all work like your own family. I came from a very dysfunctional family and worked very hard to overcome that and build something different -- so many times, this was triggering for me. I had to remind myself that it was not about me. That this family had to work it out for themselves. I had to walk away. Because ultimately, it is not the doula's job to fix it.

Another challenge was working through my husband's illness, and then trying to figure out what I was going to do to earn a living. All of a sudden, I had become the breadwinner in my family: I needed to find a job I loved that paid well and had comprehensive benefits. I did accomplish that but then terribly missed working with new families. I had to learn to move on. To find other things I could do to keep me connected with what I loved, while I was unable to practice full time as a doula.

Rosemary Mason

Rosemary Mason was a birth and postpartum doula, postpartum doula trainer and CLC until she retired in 2016. For over 22 years, she worked in San Diego, CA.

Welcome doulas, to this wonderful career.

I became a postpartum doula to teach. As a postpartum doula, I realized I was going to be directly involved in the lives of my clients and babies. My words had power and could change lives. I learned my craft. I studied and became a childbirth educator, birth doula, postpartum doula, postpartum doula trainer, breastfeeding counselor and postpartum mood disorder advisor. All these steps made me a better postpartum doula. I worked hard as my business grew. I was always trying to read more, to learn more from other doulas and professionals in the field. I learned that being a postpartum doula is not about holding a baby, but holding a place for my clients to become a family. This work is a calling. It drives you to be the best you can be.

One of the most important things I learned is to set boundaries for myself. I have seen many doulas (new and experienced) fall into this trap of being everything to their clients. I learned very early on, this was not my baby, I'm not a marriage counselor, house cleaner, general contractor, gardener, cook or massage therapist. I created a referral page with professionals that I gave out at all my interviews during my first day on the job. This keeps you in your lane and your skill set. Now, of course if you are a massage therapist, you can make an appointment or set aside time to practice this skill, but charge your regular fee and add it to your billing statement.

There was a time when you did all your communication with a client by telephone (landline). I really miss that. I felt that was my first teaching moment. Hearing a new mom's voice gave me a lot of insight as to what was happening. She may have sounded excited, crying, scared or distant. I knew it took a lot of courage for that mom to pick up the phone and call me to say she needed help. I knew my support started right then and there, before we even met. Many times it did turn into a job, but sometimes it was just a mom reaching out for some personal contact. Every contact with a mom is a teachable moment and I can talk and teach a lot in 5 minutes. So remember to teach your mom to talk -- to you, to their babies, to their families. Babies don't text or read emails but they love their mom's voice.

I ran my business as a professional postpartum doula. It took some time and a lot of effort, but in time I was able to draft a flexible contract that worked for me. I opened my own bank account, got postpartum insurance, figured out a yearly advertising budget, decided on a business name and learned about branding, started the first doula group in our city, found a person to design my website, and created a social media presence. I gave back to my community through charitable work, baby fairs, high school presentations, and our Vets. I "ate the frog" each week and went over all my business and social media presences, to keep up with the changing times.

I was a symptomatic saver, something I learned in my doula training. I saved a percentage of each of my paychecks. This job is a feast or famine. You'll have to expect some down time between jobs, illnesses, or pandemic. It's easy to save, and fun to watch your wealth grow.

One's journey to become a postpartum doula takes many twists and turns before finding the path. I know it sounds overwhelming at first, but break it down to bites. Do what works for you and your community, not what other doulas do. We have too many "Debbie Doulas" out there. Be yourself, bring your personality to your families, joke with them, listen to them. Let them know that all beginnings are hard. Parents say that babies don't come with a manual, but they do, it is called a "postpartum doula." Being their manual to turn to when they have questions is vital to a successful postpartum relationship. That's why taking postpartum training is so important. Training gives you a base to learn and grow from. Don't skip this important step.

I think some challenges may be keeping up with your education and not becoming stale in your ideas or knowledge. Don't rest on your laurels; there is always something new out there to be learned. Be it baby products, breastfeeding studies, mood disorders, changing family dynamics or reading a new book about the practice. Take time each year to attend a conference or learn a new skill. Keep your branding fresh and current. Talk and vent with other doulas. You can't do this alone.

Know your limits physically and mentally. No one can work 24/7 with multiple families for weeks on end without a break, or support from other doulas. Even Amazon employees have days off.

So many joys to count. Clients that send you cards, texts, emails and Facebook updates on their families and thank you over and over again for your support. I'm proud to be called a pioneer in this field as I can't think of a more rewarding career than being a postpartum doula. It is the best job in the world.

Kimberly Bepler, IBCLC, CPD, NPE, CLE®

Kimberly Bepler is the founder of ABC Doula in Portland, OR, and has served hundreds of families since. She specializes in twins and triplets, having served over 700 sets. Kimberly developed her own training on multiples for doulas, and is a Lactation Educator, Postpartum Doula Trainer and New Parent Educator for CAPPA. You can find out more about Kimberly at www.abcdoula.com.

I became a postpartum doula because it was a dream job from the moment I heard about this role. Helping not only new babies, but also the parents, was something I never thought possible. Nanny work was the only role I had heard of that I got to spend time with newborns, which were my favorite! Back in the days before the Internet answered all our questions, I trusted the person who told me that doula work was real, and that parents would pay a trusted caregiver to guide and educate them in the first couple months. I'm so glad I did, because she was right! I thought as a nanny I would have to stay with families for 1-2 years each time I worked with a new baby, and I think toddlers are really hard. I also love working alongside parents, rather than working on my own with a new baby, which sealed the deal for me as a doula.

Initially I thought I would do this work part-time while raising my kids, as I trained when my firstborn was only 6 months old. But after realizing the potential, not just for enjoyment (as I LOVED the job), but also for provision for our family, we quickly shifted gears. I became the full-time breadwinner while my husband decided to stay home with our almost 2-year-old. What led me to doing this work as a full time profession was the reward while helping families. This work truly makes a difference, both in measurable outcomes (like less depression/anxiety, better success with breastfeeding, and better bonding together as families) and in the intangibles like contentment in early parenting, harmony between partners, and time and space to bond deeply and learn all about their babies. I find even now the presence of a doula can slow down the experience of being on a rollercoaster of unpredictable turns and dips. Although this is hard to quantify in the prenatal time frame, being present in the postnatal period creates an entirely different experience, and one that parents recognize once they are in the midst of newborn life.

The bottom line for me is that this help -- this practical, heart-centered, and very skilled level of help -- can really make life better for families with newborns. When I can support a family to truly improve their quality of life, their enjoyment of their baby and each other -- and build a buffer of kindness, gentleness, and thoughtfulness around their healing -- better families are made. Parents are more confident and trust each other, grandparents can be included in a loving and connected way, and babies have a better experience in their first few months, too. It really makes the world a better place for everyone.

I have learned to be gentle with my clients, first and foremost. The prenatal and postpartum time frame is one where families need gentleness. Being a strong person, I found that tapping into my compassion was the best route to go right from the beginning. Yes, strength can be important when you need to make business decisions, write contracts, and deal with finances, but dealing with people requires kindness and compassion. Much of my work is validating the feelings of new parents, and for that the work needs to come from a place of wholeness -- not a wounded place. You will need to set aside your needs and wants and fully focus on your clients. I have found this is the best way to serve clients as a doula successfully, in a way that inspires referrals and creates ongoing client requests.

Being able to recognize my own biases, and identifying what I had to bring versus what I was lacking, was also extremely valuable to my work. Better yet was learning the ability to curb my judgment, see people in new and more positive ways, and be able to support them no matter their perspective or the outcome they wished for their family. This took some time! Learning *not* to take on the problems of the people around me has been a huge life lesson that has served me not only professionally but also personally.

I generally get very invested in people and this work has allowed me to pour my whole heart into meeting their needs, and then be able to detach from them when their time needing me comes to an end. This was life-changing for me personally, as I tend to want to stay connected forever, and having over 2000 clients makes that impossible.

In business, I have learned the power of listening to your clients. Not all will share constructive criticism, but when they do, taking those to heart to allow yourself to change and grow can improve your business overall. Many of the service-oriented professionals I see are very concerned with setting boundaries for themselves, and making sure this is "right for them." Although I agree with boundaries and definitely want to take care of myself and my family, I don't find the need to emphasize this to clients. I believe that focusing on the clients and trying to assess what they need is the most crucial aspect of this work. If we are too focused on ourselves, we can miss a significant part of being a doula, which is having a (well-educated and well paid) servant role to play in their homes.

This is some of my best advice:

> Don't be afraid to offer up what you have to start with, but don't pretend you know more than you do. Having a heart to help, thinking of small things you can do to care for the family, and just being present is valuable. Even when you are first beginning, charge for your time and care.
>
> Your support becomes even more valuable when you leave all your baggage at home and offer families care, regardless of their opinions on parenting or newborns. When you can drop your bias and fully support clients no matter their choices, it is a gift to them and eventually builds their confidence in their own skills, which is our long-term goal.
>
> As you notice things that need to be done, learn how to suggest what you can do without telling clients what you think is neces-

sary. If you can see that there are things you would want done, cultivate ways to ask that allow clients the opportunity to utilize you fully without any judgment. Learning to offer tasks, support, and education is a process, but being proactive can help a family get a lot more out of doula support.

Don't be afraid to be specific. One of the biggest mistakes I see with new doulas is they say, "I will do whatever you need." This sounds helpful, except that families often don't know what they need. A better approach when there is uncertainty would be to say, "I can do this, or that, or that... or something else. What sounds the most helpful for you right now?" Pinpointing the tasks can really help parents understand what you do as a doula, and also lets them know you are prioritizing what is most important to them. This is crucial for helping parents learn confidence in their own assessments.

Squeezing in education makes the doula's role more valuable than care alone, and this can be huge for new parents who have limited experience with newborns. Although humans learn primarily by watching and doing (and they will imitate the things you show them), if you can also add in research studies about things you are learning, tips on growth and development, and take the time to educate yourself on each challenge as it comes up, it can raise your value with client families. It helps families realize you are on their team, and their loyalty to you grows -- raising the referral rate for your service.

The joy of doula work explodes out of me every time I talk with someone new about becoming a doula. I can't help but tell others how satisfying it is to serve these new and vulnerable families. To be able to work with precious tiny babies and those that love them... what can I say but, WHAT AN AWESOME JOB I HAVE! Helping families successfully feed their babies, overcome challenges of crying and reflux or colic, problem solving sleep struggles, and just giving them time to nap and rest -- I love it all!

I love making them food and giving them two hands available to eat it. I love putting together a sitz bath and giving a new mother a chance to soak her aching parts. I love educating partners about the ups and downs of hormonal waves and what to expect in the first few days. I love helping grandparents enjoy their new grandbabies, and also ease the pressure of them to answer every question or do every support shift. I love setting parents up for comfort as they heal. Bringing warm delicious things to them while feeding their baby in bed. There are too many joys to count!

And there are so many challenges too: finding clients, convincing clients to book you in advance, dealing with payments/contracts/ billing, and scheduling hours that both help them and fit for you and your needs. Dealing with the cyclical nature of being your own boss is also a cause for worry; sometimes clients are flooding you with requests, sometimes nothing is coming through and you wonder if you truly are a good doula or should just go get another job. Being able to budget for things like mortgages or trips when you don't really know the income that will be coming in. The temptation to put your family needs aside and work more than you truly need because the work can be unpredictable. And those few clients that are really draining, difficult, or critical can be really tough. Sometimes the season just isn't right to do this work because of the demands of your heart, your situation, or your life responsibilities.

But when it is right, it is wonderful. It has been the joy of my life to make people's beginnings better. To help parents feel confident to do this parenting job knowing they are the right person to raise this baby. To guide them into understanding their babies, caring for themselves, and being deeply bonded to those in their family. It's still a dream job for me, 20 years later.

Marcia Thuermer, PCD/PDT(DONA), The Doula Training Path

Marcia Thuermer is a certified postpartum doula, DONA approved postpartum doula trainer, lactation consultant (IBCLC) and infant sleep coach. She found her calling in 2002 and created a lucrative and satisfying career by founding "Triangle Mothercare Inc," a doula agency in Chapel Hill, NC. Marcia sold her business, relocated to Florida and continues to train postpartum doulas under the name The Doula Training Path (formerly known as Baby Blue and Pink). https://thedoulatrainingpath.com/

I started on my path to this unbelievably fulfilling destination in 2002, and many events and decisions have led me to this place. Sometimes things happen in your life that change your perception about your world. In 2002, my sister was dying of breast cancer and my elderly father's health was failing. They both lived in two different states and far away from me. I was closely involved with -- and deeply moved emotionally by -- everything to do with the care and needs of these two important people in my life, and I had not a minute to spare in my own life.

After the deaths of these two precious people, my now-empty hours needed to be filled with meaningful new work. My life seemed bereft and I needed to do something that was nurturing and fulfilling for myself and others, something that would bring joy into a home and make a difference. I remember how difficult it was to find competent, nurturing support for my sister and father during their illness when I could not be there. I was a natural nurturer and putting them in the care of others was difficult. I had a passion to care for others and started searching for my new path.

One day a friend told me about postpartum doulas. I recalled how very difficult it was when my own son was born, and I had so little support because family members lived far away. I realized that this stop along the way on my path might be leading me to a fulfilling new life. I found DONA International and attended a postpartum doula workshop. After the training I realized that yes, nurturing and supporting mothers, babies and other family members was my calling. What a perfect and joyful decision that was. I knew I had found my path.

Being a doula going on 19 years so far, I have learned how important it is to set professional and personal boundaries. I have set professional boundaries by not making any assumptions or judgement of my clients or fellow doulas. Being non-judgmental sounds easy but it isn't. It starts with your thoughts and we may not always voice these out loud, but it still affects us. It's like implicit or unconscious bias, as we are influenced by our experiences and upbringing. We can diminish it through awareness and openness. By recognizing and acknowledging it, we can let go and give people the unconditional support they need and want. This is what makes a great doula.

As for personal boundaries, it's so important to take care of yourself and your own families, too. If you don't take care of yourself, you can't care for others. Midway through my career I lost sight of this and was working way too many hours and it began to affect my work. I was trying to do everything myself. I have always been physically healthy but emotionally I was becoming very stressed out and it started showing. After two colleagues told me I was getting burned out, I knew I had to make a change. I loved this career, but I was putting everyone first and not nurturing myself or spending time with my own family. I made some changes by delegating to others, hiring more doulas and spending time doing other things I loved. By reprioritizing, I worked my way back to a healthy situation and my business flourished. I was a happy person and I realized that there were other parts of this career I wanted to focus on.

My advice to a new doula just starting out is "Don't let other people steal your dreams." So many people told me this is a great career, but you won't make any money doing it. People can't afford your services; it is a good thing you have a spouse to support you. I'm glad I was smart enough *not* to listen to them. My motto and an affirmation I have had for most of my adult life is "Do what you love, and the money will come." I did not get into this career to get rich, however, I valued myself and knew I could earn a living being a postpartum doula. You need to come from an abundant thought process.

Thoughts create Feelings
Feelings create Actions
Actions create Results
Results create Success

Never give up and set "right for you" goals. Realistic goals that are achievable. Write them down and tackle them one step at a time. Do something every day that will get you closer to your goal(s) no matter how small that task is. You can start out with just one or two simple goals and make a step-by-step plan on how to get there. Once achieved, set more goals. Start small and build.

Fear is the only thing that can stop you! When you have a plan, the fear is diminished.

Sometimes as a new postpartum doula, it is easy to feel not good enough. You may believe that because you are not certified, you should offer your services for a deeply discounted price. I believe it is important to help others, especially under-resourced clients. There are many ways to give back and make sure you do. However, you do not have to give everything away. Find a balance between helping people that need you with little or no resources by discounting or volunteering your services and helping people that need you with many resources and can afford your fees. When you are successful, you can help more people that are in need.

Finally, network, network, network! And ask for help when you get stuck.

My joys are many.

A favorite quote of mine from an anonymous author is, "When you are a caregiver, you know that every day you will touch a life, or a life will touch yours."

This is the joy of being a postpartum doula for me. Every new family is an opportunity to *give* and to *receive*. To each family I give my best loving care and skills to bring peace and calm into their sometimes not-so-calm new environment. Empowering parents to make their own right choices and give them the confidence to be the best parents they can be. And what do I receive? At the end of the day I feel grateful, joyful, and appreciated.

Each new baby brings a special light and unconditional love into the world. It is my blessing to share with them in that light.

The things that challenge me the most are my time and priorities. It is easy for me to shut down after working with a family or ignore administrative duties that are a part of running and improving my business. I am a professional and treat my business as one of my top priorities along with my own family. As a doula, I like to make myself available to families if they need extra help. As a postpartum doula trainer, I am always looking for ways to improve my teaching skills and help students become successful. Finding a balance is important in this type of work.

We not only nurture others, but need to nurture our own selves. Keeping the passion alive requires some discipline. That is what keeps me going and it's important, so I don't get burned out. By setting goals, defining my priorities, and making time for both work and pleasure, I feel balanced. Whether that pleasure is self-care, family time, exercise, or other hobbies -- they are all important to have a balanced, successful and joyful life.

Sonya Duffee, CLD, CLDT, HCHD, CCBE, CPD

Sonya Duffee is the grandmother of three little ones and mother of two daughters. For 22 years she has dedicated her life to serving birthing families through pregnancy, birth and postpartum. She is a CAPPA-certified labor doula and postpartum doula, as well a CAPPA-certified childbirth educator, and faculty for CAPPA's labour doula and postpartum doula program. https://www.fullcirclebirthcollective.com/sonya-duffee.html

I became a postpartum doula because I noticed many families were not getting the support they envisioned as they were navigating parenthood and healing from their birth experience. They were not being fully equipped with the essentials for a smooth transition.

With many families not having family or friends available to assist their immediate needs, this period of adjustment and learning leaves many isolated and tending to everything alone, without a support network to nourish and care for them. New parents are being left with little guidance, reassurance and encouragement as they tend to their newborn and the adaptation it brings. They usually feel this burden greatly on top of sleep deprivation, as well as mental and physical fatigue. As an experienced birth worker,

I knew that this was an area that would greatly impact the new parent's experience. I believe that the more they are cared for and supported the better they will be as parents.

Becoming a postpartum doula or any kind of doula is a lesson in self-discovery of your own views, attitudes and beliefs: how we communicate and interact with families, noticing if we are placing judgement, and allowing new parents to build trust in themselves and their own beliefs. We must always remember that in order to fully embrace our clients in their personal journey and growth, we must step back and allow them to come to a place of understanding and exploration of what they feel is best for them. We must remain neutral in our discussions providing information and guidance that helps them foster a deep understanding of their baby and needs. The relationship between a doula and their client gives us feedback on our approach.

Being a doula is one thing and being a business owner is another. Your mindset can impact your progression. Give yourself the same grace as you would give your clients in learning new things. It will take time to build your reputation and referral system, and usually business owners find it takes about two years of consistent working to establish oneself. Keep holding the vision of what you wish to create in your business, and take those steps daily through networking, connecting with your community and colleagues. Don't let fear stop you from moving forward, and don't expect to know it all. Continue learning the ins and outs of this profession. Don't take it personally when not hired. You may never know the reasons why the people who you are meant to work with will find you. There will never be a shortage of people having babies.

One of my biggest challenges has been keeping current on social media platforms, and learning how to create visual content to help promote my business and what I do. Navigating the learning curve of advertising and reaching potential clients takes time. Of course, the joys have been seeing birthing women conquer birth and empower themselves, claiming the strength within and overcoming their fears as they journey through pregnancy, birth and the postpartum period. There are many rewards that come with being in a profession that truly feels like you are making a difference.

Chapter 4 - Doula History And Philosophy

In the 1600s and 1700s, in the United States, reciprocal care (neighbor helping neighbor) was the norm. There was no hired help. Women were surrounded by other women in a familiar environment for birthing and the postpartum period. Friends and family were present, and supported the woman throughout the birth and in the weeks and months that followed. Midwives attended a majority of births.

There were no standards or formal education on birthing. Women learned from each other, and supported loved ones through the birth process. There were some apprenticeships available with more experienced midwives.

Somewhere in the 1760s American women invited male physicians into the birthing room. Dr. William Shippen brought obstetrics to the United States, after he was trained in midwifery overseas. He taught both male and female midwives. Later, he limited the teaching to only males.

As cities grew, people began to purchase services for postpartum care. In Boston in the 1770s, middle class women hired nurses and household help for postpartum support. Immigrant communities still adopted the social childbirth approach until they became Americanized.

It's important to note the shift from woman-to-woman support, where female midwives attended most of the births, to male-dominated obstetrics. This is what led to the pain-free childbirth movement in the early 19th century.

A six to eight week lying-in period was still popular in Colonial times in the USA. Neighbors did everything: chores, sibling care, meals. At the end of the period, there was a big celebration called a groaning party. Nobody knows whether it was because the table groaned with food or whether the groaning refers to labor. The new mother would invite all of the women who had helped her during the birth and the lying-in period, and they would have a woman's festival, which has all but disappeared in modern times.

By 1900, most middle class women made arrangements for help after birth, from either a friend or relative. It was not always an ideal situation, but women felt secure -- not isolated like they sometimes feel today. Twilight Sleep became popular around 1914 because pain was the most feared aspect of birth. The fact is that many women still experienced pain, even with the Scopolamine and morphine cocktail they were given. Lots of women became addicted to morphine due to the widespread use for postpartum recovery. In some cases, newborn babies suffered from asphyxiation.

In the 1920s, childbirth moved to the hospitals. Childbirth was considered a pathological process, instead of a natural event. It was more convenient for doctors to centralize their activities, modeling a system for labor and birth after the assembly line. Strangers now cared for women. Feminists advocated completely unconscious birth.

With urbanization came an increase in hospital births. By 1935, approximately 75% of all births occurred in the hospital. The depression and then World War II saw a decline in hired household help. This, along with medical advancements, fueled the trend of the hospital as the place to be for postpartum recovery.

Postpartum care in the hospital became a recovery period from a medical procedure, rather than a replacement for domestic assistance. Yet, World War II also caused a great shift in hospital personnel, and a questioning of the ten to 14-day postpartum stay.

By the 1950s, consumers began to advocate for natural childbirth, thereby reclaiming ownership of their birthing experience. They began to reject the unconscious, medicated birth. Women were released from the hospital in less than a week. Some women were passive and not inclined toward natural childbirth, but still questioned the hospital control on their childbirth experience. For those that could afford it, the live-in baby nurse became very popular.

In the 1960s fathers and partners became more involved in

the process, though they were not yet in the birthing room. Preparation for birth did not always prepare the couple for the postpartum period. Much like it is today, it was difficult to find extended family and neighbors willing to help out. Some women didn't want the help, becoming very independent.

The 1970s saw a rise in the women's movement, and with that, a movement to take back reproductive health. Women challenged the status quo of obstetric care and postpartum care. They pushed back against the limited visitors and restricted contact with their newborn babies. We saw men in the birthing room. This is the time when Dana Raphael wrote her book that I mentioned earlier.

By the 1980s, our lives had become much more complex. We had to choose between staying home or having a career. Perhaps doing both, and becoming torn about priorities, and financial well-being. Old traditions and rituals were completely forgotten. We reached the pinnacle of the "I can do it myself" attitude. Choices about postpartum care became available. There were a lot of studies about separation of the MotherBaby, and the detrimental effects of that on the newborn baby.

Early discharge programs were popular. Many came with follow-up care from postpartum nurses, and outpatient clinics for mothers and babies. These mothers who agreed to the early discharge were typically low-risk. Soon this became the norm, as it was considered safe.

In the 1990s, "Drive-Thru Deliveries" became a common phenomenon. Most insurance companies were only covering a 24-hour stay for vaginal birth and a 72-hour stay for cesarean section births. There wasn't adequate observation and education of expectations for the postpartum period; for the MotherBaby.

In the 2000s, there began a rapid rise in the cesarean section rate. The national average in 2007 was 32 percent -- a 53 percent increase from 1996 to 2007 -- and the highest rate ever. It is the most common surgery performed in the United States. At the same time, the labor induction rates have more than doubled, from 9.5 percent in 1990 to roughly 30 percent in 2014. In 2016, the national cesarean rate hovered around 32 percent and has plateaued in the last couple of years. There have been some studies that suggest the induction of labor plays a role in the cesarean section rate. You can research that one.

Unfortunately -- despite our technology and our riches -- as of 2017, the U.S. was behind the leading industrialized nations of Canada, Italy, Spain, Germany, Japan, the U.K., and Portugal in the number of babies dying in the first year of life. **And in 2019, the United States earned the reputation of being the most dangerous place to give birth among developed nations, with a rising maternal mortality rate.**

Many of these deaths (nearly 60 percent) are preventable. Two thirds of the deaths occur at birth or within the first year after birth. This is why it is critical that women receive support during the postpartum period, as well as follow-up care. They deserve the education and information about what to watch for, including signs of infection or other abnormalities.

The College of Obstetricians and Gynecologists (ACOG) came out with new guidelines in 2018, stressing that women should be seen within the first three weeks after birth, and that postpartum care is an ongoing process. This is a shift from the standard six week follow-up visit.

Medical interventions save lives, but the question we need to ask is whether routine medical intervention is necessary for everyone. **Despite the fact that the midwifery model of care produces the best outcomes for mothers and babies, the obstetrical model of care is still the most prominent in the United States.**

The interventions used during birth, such as cesarean surgery, Pitocin, epidural, and vacuum extraction, have residual effects on a woman's recovery in the postpartum period -- both physically and emotionally. Increased risk of infection, inhibited breastfeeding, headaches, injury to the perineum, and interference in bonding are all possible consequences, depending on the intervention.

Unfortunately, breastfeeding efforts may fail with a lack of support. Women are left to search for support themselves. Even though breastfeeding rates have improved over the years, families are miles apart and moms and in-laws are not always educated about breastfeeding. Hospital staff knowledge of breastfeeding varies widely, and could lead to wrong information.

If breastfeeding starts with challenges that aren't managed properly, it can be difficult for Mom. Bottles are given readily and in some cases, routinely. Mom's milk does not come in until the third day or so, and she may not know how to deal with engorgement, how to manage feedings according to her baby, or know what to do for a weak suck or sleepy baby.

In addition, information regarding caring for the baby and for the mother is too overwhelming for Mom and her partner or support person to process. Routine discharge planning -- with the inclusion of community resources for challenges that arise with breastfeeding and emotional adjustment issues -- needs to be standard protocol in every facility where mothers give birth.

Although some hospitals have a discharge plan that includes community resources for families, this is not standard practice.

There is clearly a lack of support in the United States, for the job of mothering and parenting.

The word doula was coined in the 1970s by Dana Raphael in her book, *The Tender Gift: Breastfeeding*. It was meant to describe a woman who nurtures, guides, and supports other women with breastfeeding and mothering, including labor support. In more recent times, the doula has been associated with a woman (sometimes a man) who supports a woman or couple through labor and birth. The birth doula, as it has come to be known, is there during pregnancy, labor and birth to answer questions and provide non-medical support.

A postpartum doula is the one who provides practical, emotional, and physical support to the new mother and family after birth, or during the fourth trimester. She is part of the village that doesn't exist anymore. What exactly is her scope of practice, and what is her role?

I recently learned that Dana Raphael also coined the term *matresence*, which is making a comeback. This is the process of becoming a mother. She explained how there isn't a moment of becoming a mother, but rather a process or a journey. Think of adolescence, when the hormones and the brain are going through major shifts. When we can correlate becoming a mother in this same way, we can talk to expectant mothers before birth, and help them set realistic expectations. There are so many changes happening simultaneously; physical, mental, spiritual, emotional. Relationship with self and others.

It's really a metamorphosis of sorts, like the caterpillar who becomes a butterfly. Your job is to be there for that process ideally in the beginning to be a guide, and source of support. I'm calling this process for you becoming a postpartum doula, *doularesence*. It's not overnight, or even over a week or a year, in which you suddenly become a doula.

The postpartum doula's focus is on the mother primarily, as well as her family. This does not mean there is no baby care involved. It does mean that what the mother needs and wants is what the doula focuses on. First time mothers are often unsure about everything. The postpartum doula can guide them to their confidence, their inner knowing. The doula could also do laundry and prepare a meal. It varies with each client, and each situation, and each day for the same client.

You get to choose the services you provide within a non-medical capacity. There are many roles and services that are possible with each family. It is up to you to determine those needs with guidance from your client. And you can establish everything up front. If you have other skills and degrees or certifications, you can offer those to your clients.

This is not rocket science, and the more knowledge you have about pregnancy, birth, and the fourth trimester, the more you can support your clients with their needs. You get to tailor your services however it works for you. Generally speaking, breastfeeding support, facilitation of bonding, nutrition, and healing and comfort are key for the new mother. Many postpartum doulas do laundry and light chores.

New mothers, in an ideal world, are focused on their own healing after birth, and getting to know their baby. When this is happening from the beginning of the fourth trimester, the transition into motherhood is easier.

Many people are confused about the difference between a postpartum doula and a baby nurse. The baby nurse, who isn't a licensed nurse most of the time, focuses on the baby. Usually she does the baby's laundry, bathes the baby, sleeps in the same room as the baby, and encourages sleep for the mother. The main distinction is that with this focus, facilitation of bonding and attachment isn't always happening. There is often more separation of the MotherBaby dyad. The postpartum doula encourages bonding and rest.

This is critical in caring for the MotherBaby couple because a baby doesn't know they are a separate human being from their mother. It is the most important knowledge to acquire, as the baby's development into a trusting human being begins very early. The baby's brain is wiring rapidly, and first impressions and experiences have a profound effect on how that baby develops, even in the womb.

Whatever services you offer, one of the keys is to first decide who your clients are. This will not be every pregnant woman. It may take some time to figure this out. Eventually, you will know who your ideal client is, as you begin to work with different families. You may already know.

Remember, your role as a postpartum doula is mainly about guidance and support. You offer all that you know when asked, and asking questions of your clients is how you can facilitate them coming to their own conclusions and answers. It is all about them finding and trusting their own answers. Parents are the experts on their baby, not you.

When you come from a space of love, acceptance, and true heart-centered support, you will be providing what your clients need and want from a non-judgmental perspective. If you find yourself judging, take a step back and ask yourself how you can put yourself in your client's perspective. And, if this is challenging, you get to figure out why. Left unchecked, this judgement will interfere in your ability to do your job and provide what is needed to serve your clients 100 percent.

The First Three Months of Motherhood, the Fourth Trimester of Childbirth (Beginning of Matresence)

Doulas, both birth and postpartum, do their best to help prepare mothers and families for the transformational event of becoming parents. It can be challenging because there is a greater emphasis on preparing for birth. Doulas are focused on the new mother primarily, though support of fathers or partners is also part of the job.

While I do believe there is much you can do to prepare, I don't believe you can ever be completely prepared for motherhood. I believe the toughest job you'll ever love is the job of mother, Mom, Mommy.

No matter what your client's situation is, planning is great, but knowing certain universal truths about becoming a mother is also valuable. Honestly, knowing how to handle stress and how to get the most sleep are most important. Most of all, it's vital to gather and enroll a support team.

These are a few things you can share with your clients to help them prepare before the baby arrives:

> You can tell them they will spend many hours feeding, rocking, diapering, bathing and playing with their baby.
>
> You can let them know that sleep is one of the key ingredients in feeling comfortable and confident.
>
> You can discuss any risk factors for a mood disorder (this is the most common complication of childbirth).
>
> You can encourage them to create their support team, to line it up ahead of time, and to share with their doula.
>
> You can suggest discussing expectations with their partner, and learn about what they may be experiencing in anticipation of the baby coming.

Help your clients with setting realistic expectations. They may not be aware that newborns do not sleep eight hours in a row or that their baby's stomach is the size of a walnut and she can only take in a couple of teaspoons at a time for the first few days. Don't assume what your clients know and what they don't know.

Let parents know that their emotions may be all over the place. They might feel happy, sad, frustrated, tired, or angry -- or maybe all at the same time. Always start with where they're at in terms of concerns, questions, knowledge and comfort level with newborns. This will guide you with what to say and do.

Most countries provide between three months and one year of full-time equivalent paid leave. Sweden provides 40 weeks of full-time equivalent paid leave. **The United States is one of only two countries to offer no paid parental leave, except for some federal employees.** Australia also offers no paid leave, but supports new parents with a substantial financial "baby bonus" regardless of whether they take parental leave.

Postpartum Care and The Postpartum Doula In The United States Today

The lack of support for women and families during the postpartum period gives rise to many concerns, including (but not limited to):

little time to assess feeding problems
post-birth infections going unnoticed
newborn jaundice
pre-eclampsia

With local extended families virtually extinct, and communities often made up of people who don't know each other, support is difficult to find. Our busy lifestyles prevent us from being neighborly. Other cultures, where support systems are in place, have lower incidences of postpartum depression than we do in the United States.

In most societies, the postpartum period is time to recuperate. There is a recognition of the changing roles of mothers and their partners. In countries with low rates of postpartum depression, there is a great deal of personal attention given to the new mother. Rituals and ceremonies exist. In the U.S., many rituals and traditions surrounding childbirth and the postpartum period are no longer practiced.

There are groups of women in various communities who do continue to offer ceremonies, food trains, and support. We need more of that.

With the increased need to help families, the doula has become increasingly popular, for both labor support and postpartum care. It is an old tradition renewed.

The postpartum doula takes the place of absent family members and lost communities. Much like the labor doula, the postpartum caregiver's role is to comfort, guide, and educate. The doula also provides support in the home in terms of household organization. Individual doulas and doula services vary on exactly which services are provided.

Each case is different because each MotherBaby and family is different.

Women who have just given birth are going through tremendous physical and emotional adjustments. The postpartum doula is there to take care of the new mother and her family. **The doula tunes in to what the new mother needs, because she doesn't always know what she needs.** Alleviating the stresses of life with a newborn is the doula's job. Her presence should be a calming influence on a sometimes very chaotic time in a family's life.

A doula addresses the many physical, emotional, practical and educational needs of mothers and their families, where health care providers and hospitals are falling short. A doula can guide a new mother through the abundance of information given to her from the hospital, from cord care to diapering to bathing. Some mothers feel very confident about handling their baby, but some are very unsure and uneasy handling their newborn.

Breastfeeding support is of utmost importance. Direct baby care may or may not be a priority. How much contact the doula actually has with the baby will depend on the mother's comfort level with her newborn. The mother's priorities should be the doula's priorities. If the mother is nurtured, she can better nurture her baby. Emotional support for the new mother can prevent depression and feelings of isolation, and can also boost confidence levels.

And, of course, the more rest and sleep a new mother gets, the better she feels. The physical support in the home is very important and can be a lifesaver for a mother who has no family around to assist her.

The doula must always be nonjudgmental and supportive of her client's choices, whether she agrees with them or not. Doulas provide unbiased information, and the new mother and family will make decisions that work best for them.

The doula can:

Instill confidence in a new mother.

Offer choices, suggestions of what's been done, and refer to books and other evidence-based sources that offer solutions.

Praise a Mom for her good job.

Help a Mom tune into her own gut reactions about things. Some find this right away, while others need a lot of guidance.

Remind a Mom that she and her partner are the best decision-makers about care for their baby. They know their baby better than anyone else, including the pediatrician.

The doula must keep in mind that although her knowledge may be abundant, she is a non-medical support provider. She should never diagnose a medical problem, or prescribe medicine or herbs without a proper license or certification. Always refer questions of a medical nature back to the medical provider (obstetrician, midwife or pediatrician). The doula shouldn't be afraid to say she doesn't know something, and be willing to find out what she doesn't know by making a phone call or referring to a particular book, provider, evidence-based website or other resource.

Chapter 5 - Roles And Responsibilities Of The Postpartum Doula

Educator. Day-to-day care such as bathing, diapering and cord care can be intimidating to some new parents. The doula teaches the new mother and father about normal newborn behavior and reassures the new parents that everything is okay. With a hands-on teacher, parents can learn more easily in the comfort of their own home. Although hospitals teach parents before they are sent home with their baby, the amount of information is overwhelming immediately following childbirth. Breastfeeding is also a skill that sometimes requires a little bit of teaching, including showing the new mother positioning and proper latch-on technique.

There are many other topics a doula can educate new parents on such as: bonding and attachment, safety, physical changes after birth, and emotional adjustment. The key is for the doula to learn all she can, and know where to look for the best available evidence-based information when she does not have an answer. And, remind parents to trust their own instincts.

Mother Care. The most important thing a doula does is care for the new mother, with nutrition, rest, reassurance, encouragement, reminders to take care of any physical problems (hemorrhoids, episiotomies, sore nipples), or whatever else is needed to help Mom relax so she can breastfeed and take care of baby. If not breastfeeding, Mom still needs this support. Some new mothers need to be reminded to eat and to rest.

While a new mother is busy learning to care for her newborn, she needs someone to nurture her. From serving meals, to setting up a nursing corner, the doula can provide the new mother with the support necessary to assist with a positive breastfeeding relationship between mother and baby. This emotional support can make all the difference in the world to a new mother who is beginning her journey into motherhood.

Breastfeeding Support. This is a big part of the doula's job. All doulas should have a basic knowledge of breastfeeding. Some doulas have a broader knowledge base than others, depending on experience. Doulas should be able to guide and assist the mother with positioning and latch-on to prevent sore nipples and engorgement. As a doula gains more experience, she should be able to recognize signs and symptoms of possible problems such as engorgement, sore nipples, improper sucking, weak sucking and blocked milk ducts. If problems go beyond the doula's realm of knowledge, she should call in a lactation consultant, La Leche League leader or if necessary, a medical doctor. When in doubt, refer out!

Child Care. If there are older siblings in the home, the doula may be hired to entertain them while the mother is nursing and tending to her newborn. Older siblings are adjusting to receiving less attention than they are accustomed to. Having someone to play with can help ease this adjustment. On the other hand, it may be that the older sibling requires the mother's attention and the doula cares for the newborn directly, while the mother plays with her older child(ren). If a baby is high need (crying a lot and/or needing to be held), it can be very frustrating. Thoughts of harming the baby in this situation are very common. Having someone else to hand the baby to, someone there to say, "it's okay," and being able to rest or take a break is a relief for a mother in this situation.

The doula helps the mother to balance her time and energy among her children. This is often very difficult in the early weeks postpartum. Without help, the new family can become quite fatigued and overwhelmed.

Resource and Referral Source. This is perhaps the most important aspect of the doula's job. When a situation she encounters is beyond her realm of knowledge and scope of practice, the doula needs to know what is available in her community to refer the family to, such as pediatricians, lactation consultants, Baby and

Me classes, single parent groups, and Mom's clubs. The doula is often the only link a new family has. The relationship between the doula and the mother and father sometimes lasts beyond the actual working relationship. Calls may come weeks and months later when a new family is seeking other assistance.

Active Listener. The doula is by no means a professional counselor, although some doulas may have a counseling background. Sometimes a doula just listens. This is a skill that often takes some time to develop. Mom may need to share her birth story or her own feelings of insecurity. Oftentimes, there are family problems that come to the forefront when a child is born: marital issues, relationships with parents, grief over a recent death, financial difficulties, feelings of inadequacy, etc. The new mother needs someone to talk to who will listen without judgment. The doula is there for this. **Just having somebody present and not feeling isolated greatly reduces the stress of certain environmental factors that can contribute to baby blues or depression.**

Household Organizer. This role varies depending on the needs of the new family. Most doulas will do laundry, prepare simple meals, run errands, and perform day-to-day tasks such as emptying trash and washing dishes. This is an invaluable service to the new mother. She shouldn't be doing anything except caring for her newborn and herself. Chores and other physical work should be avoided for at least several weeks. This is especially true when the mother has given birth by cesarean section. Sleep deprivation requires that Mother naps when possible, and reserves energy for caring for her baby. If the mother is breastfeeding, it is particularly important that she eat balanced, nutritious meals, as her body uses extra calories to produce milk for the baby.

The doula also gives dads a chance to bond and to spend time with their partner, without having to think about the daily chores. He also needs his sleep and relaxation.

Mediator. This role does come up sometimes. Oftentimes a new mother is being torn in different directions by well-meaning members of her extended family. Everyone has some advice for her. The doula will often be the go-between when this circumstance arises. She may be able to put out a fire or prevent one before it begins. The doula often provides up-to-date information about newborn care and breastfeeding so the relatives know what current evidence shows. The last thing a new mother needs is any additional pressure, besides those that come with a "normal" transition into motherhood.

Public Education and Outreach. All of us need to educate our providers, legislators, and the expectant and new parents we work with. It is our duty to pass on knowledge. Informed decisions by parents, and well-thought out policies regarding birthing, breastfeeding, and postpartum care are critical for women to regain control of the birth process. Insurance coverage and increased demand for doula services is a sure sign that we are on our way to achieving this goal.

The doula faces her own set of challenges while helping the new mother. These include:

letting go when the job is over
not bringing the job home
communicating effectively with clients
supporting choices the doula doesn't agree with
adapting to a wide range of personalities
adapting to a variety of circumstances
emotional giving
bottle-feeding challenges
loss of a baby

In summary, with the help of a doula a new mother can:

gain confidence in her mothering abilities
establish successful feeding and care for her baby
get adequate rest and nutrition
spend time with other family members
help her partner get to know the baby
take time to heal physically
adjust better emotionally to life with a newborn

Chapter 6 - Doula Training And Certification

Only you know if you are ready to serve as a doula. There are no licensing and regulations for the doula profession. **What began as a woman-centered movement to recreate the lost village has become a career or a business for many.** It is awesome to witness this boom, and to see doulas more well-known and available to serve.

At the same time, being a doula does not necessarily require hours and hours of training. **The original birth doula studies showed significant improvements in outcomes when women were simply in the room with the laboring woman.**

The questions I hear most often are: "Which organization should I train with?" and "Do I need to be certified?"

The answers are not necessarily black and white. I always say that the training you take is as good as the trainer. It helps if they are backed by a reputable organization, or if they have years of experience as a doula and a trainer. With so many trainings and certifications to choose from, it can be very confusing for new and aspiring doulas.

I was a postpartum doula trainer for the two organizations that have been around the longest. DONA International and CAPPA. I chose to branch out on my own to teach because I like to say what I want without restriction. My teaching style is more about intimate connection and being a mentor throughout the process. This is missing in a lot of larger organizations.

When considering a training, find out about the trainer. Ask her how long she has been a doula, how long she has been training and what her doula philosophy is. Also, find out about the organization, or the people behind it.

Looks can be deceiving. It's easy to look great online, like the best of the best. Cost can be a factor, but don't be fooled by a high or a low price tag. Remember that most organizations require a certification fee, and require you to recertify and maintain membership. Some organizations give lifetime certification. Trust yourself to choose wisely.

In my humble opinion, what matters the most in training is the emphasis on continuing education. **Staying current and relevant with the latest research -- as well as being plugged in to what parents are reading and watching -- will help you as you grow.**

Do some research, ask others, and reach out to talk to the trainer directly. Just like choosing clients and them choosing you, there has to be a connection. Something about the training, the trainer, or the organization will resonate with you. Trifecta, if it all aligns with your needs.

Trust your inner guidance system. This is exactly what you want for the women you're or will be serving. I want to emphasize this point. There are possibly ten different answers, from ten people you ask about who to train with or how to get started. Everyone thinks their training is the best, or the organization they are affiliated with is the best. It is the best for them, and it is probably a great training and organization.

You'll want to spend some time asking yourself a lot of questions. For example:

What do I really want from a training?

What am I able to commit to, in terms of time and energy?

How do I learn best -- Online? In person? A combination of both?

What will my budget allow?

Consider reading stories from longtime postpartum doulas, to learn about their journeys, lessons learned, and the joys and challenges of this incredible profession. I purposefully asked doulas from different organizations and backgrounds to contribute. Some are independent. Some I have a personal connection with. All of these are meant to help you as you navigate your personal journey and decision to become a postpartum doula. I want you to notice the differences in their experiences, and how they came to this work.

I want you to recognize when something resonates with you or inspires you. Also, to recognize when you have a gut feeling of yes or no. This is what will guide you to do what is best for you -- not what anybody else says you "should" do.

There are many doulas who work without having been trained or certified. This is not right or wrong. Perhaps they have life experience that qualifies them. Clients will ideally be asking lots of questions of you, as their potential doula, before they hire anyone.

Some of the questions clients may ask you include the following:

What is your training?
What is your background?
How long have you been doing this work?
What brought you to this work?
Do you work with anybody?
What is your parenting philosophy?

Experience counts for a lot, and connection is key. The postpartum doula will feel like a good fit, or not. This client will be a good fit for you, or not. Trust yourself to know.

Mothering a mother always requires an open heart, a listening ear, and helping hands. This is the essence of being a doula.

Chapter 7 - Being Successful On Your Terms

It is in the very definition of something where the answers can be vastly different.

Success is setting an intention or a goal, and then achieving it. It has everything to do with doing what you say you are going to do, and getting what you say you want.

In 2015, I took a road trip to sell my original board game, Down the Canal – the Game of Birth. My intention during this trip was to create fun and connection, plant seeds for future growth, get the game in more hands in more places, and get in front of people sharing my vision for the game. I did all of that, and gained clarity around what I really wanted at that time. I continually define and redefine my goals to get clear on my next course of action.

Many people asked me, upon my return, if I had a successful trip. I answered, "It depends on your definition of success." We all know that in our culture, success is often measured by our bank accounts. In that case, I would have probably said, "No, it was not a successful trip." Yet, I measure my success by setting intentions, taking action and seeing results. So, yes. This trip was absolutely a success.

I invite you to consider where you are now with your personal, financial or business goals. Then, create an intention for the day, the week, the month, and long term. You can also write a vision of what the day, week, or month feels like. Get it out on paper -- write it or draw it. Keep it in front of you and refer to it daily. Take action every day that aligns with your intention, and your vision.

You get to define your own success, rather than your success being defined by those around you -- or by what our culture says about success. This can be challenging when others around you are constantly asking what you're doing, and if you're working, and how much money you're making. It's none of their business.

Create a roadmap for yourself. Remember your big why, and think big. Get clear on what you really want. Make commitments and establish deadlines. Hire a coach, or join a group of other doulas supporting one another. If there isn't one, create it.

There is no shame in seeking support. That is another cultural phenomenon, where we think we can do it all, and that we "should" be doing more. Stop "shoulding" on yourself. Instead, think about and visualize what you could do.

The most important thing to know is that you can figure it out or get help. Postpartum doulas are a guide, a listening ear, and a warm heart. Yet, there is always stuff to know about -- and much of the secret is in knowing what you don't know!

When I started my journey in 1991, things were a lot simpler. There was no certification. Imagine that. I had a boss, who became my mentor. I took a basic CPR/First Aid course, and a breastfeeding workshop with a La Leche League leader. I shadowed a postpartum doula. We had ongoing staff meetings centered on different topics. We knew what to watch for in terms of emotions, and physical recovery. We also used common sense.

I learned the most in my first six months on the job. Two dehydrated babies, and bleeding nipples included. My instincts kicked in, I called people who knew more than me, and I was able to say and do what was needed in these cases. Sometimes you just have to jump in and get started. With any new endeavor, it takes time to build confidence. Learning to trust yourself is a main factor in your success.

Fast forward to modern day, there are over a hundred organizations that certify postpartum doulas. On one hand that's awesome; there are lots of choices for those that want to be postpartum doulas. On the other hand, it can be very confusing for someone starting out.

How do you know where to get your education? Which organizations back-up what they promise? Which training and philosophy resonates most with you?

More importantly, where are you in *your* journey? I guarantee you already know a lot of stuff about a lot of things. Start there. Before you sign up for a class or a program, be sure it's the right fit for you. Think about whether you'll be a solopreneur in business, or if it's better for you to work for somebody else (an agency perhaps).

There are so many ways you can be in business, or not be in business. There are postpartum doulas who market themselves just as they are. No fancy name, or website. This is how I started. You still have this option.

What I've noticed is that many new doulas (or wannabe doulas) take a lot of courses, and forget that networking, introducing yourself in your community, and connecting with other birth workers is just as important. People have to know who you are and what you have to offer.

Being a postpartum doula is different from running a business. You must do both if you want to make a living from this. Striking a balance between working *in* the business and *on* the business is key.

I remember a time when I had eight postpartum doulas I could call on to serve a client (they were independent contractors). I was being a doula (birth and postpartum), fielding calls, doing bookkeeping, as well as scheduling. My husband asked me one day, "When will you ever not be on the computer, the phone, or be out working?"

This was the moment I realized I had not found a balance. I knew I had to cut back somewhere. I chose to forgo being an on-call birth doula. My passion had always been about taking care of new mothers and families. This was the right choice for me.

We are always faced with choices. If you're struggling with something, the best thing you can do is go within. **Stop asking everyone what they think you should do, and ask yourself what you really want** -- or what the best option is. You may not get an immediate answer. It's often in the silence, or when we step back from the struggle of trying to figure it out, that the answer comes.

Families are also challenged with choices about what to do, and who to listen to. Sometimes it's a medical problem which requires the doctor. Other times, it's a choice that requires communication between mother and father (partner). Sometimes they turn to their postpartum doula for the answer.

It's not your job to provide an answer, but to ask questions. Ask them how they feel, what they want, and if they need more information to make a choice. You may find yourself wanting to give an opinion, but it doesn't belong. This is about them, not you. Perhaps you can suggest what you've been practicing: going within.

I've found that most of the time when asked a question, the new mother already knows and is seeking validation. Sometimes, there truly is a factual answer. What I most want for new mothers is for them to trust themselves to be exactly who they need to be for their baby. When mothers are born, they are learning so much about themselves in the process. Often, there's much doubt about their ability to do a good job.

You get to be their cheerleader and role model. Encourage them to go within, to trust and to surrender. Joy is possible in the early parenting experience -- especially when a person is able to let go of how they think it should be, and accept how it is.

Ten Tips for Success

1) Learn to be a chameleon. Chameleons fit in seamlessly with the environment, actually changing colors so as not to be noticed. I'm not saying to be invisible. It's more about being unobtrusive. Your clients will know you are there for what they need. How will they know this? It can be as simple as you asking them, "What do you need today?" You will work with a variety of personalities and lifestyles, many that are very different from your own. The faster you learn about your clients, the easier it will be to tend to their needs. You will encounter the list writer: neat, organized and orderly. And you will encounter the frantic, out of control, anxious new mom. Who do you get to be with each of these people? It's very likely that you will shift your focus to adapt to each unique client. And you will learn a tremendous amount about yourself in this process. This is when you utilize your ability to be a neutral observer, to really recognize why you're there at this time with this family. What is the best use of your time, energy and expertise?

2) Be excited about your new best friend: your local resources. You get to know where to refer your clients for what. This could be anything from a breastfeeding friendly pediatrician, to a home-based day care. You may be the only source this new mother and family has for information. Know where to find new mothers groups, La Leche League, and Mommy and Me classes. Get to know the people who run or own these groups and businesses. These are people and places you would go to for your own needs. **These people will become your greatest referral sources.** Breastfeeding support is one of the most important jobs you have. In addition to taking classes, reading, and attending La Leche League or other groups for familiarity, it is great to know a breastfeeding professional to whom you can ask questions. When you have an established relationship, you can check in to see if you are on the right track with a challenging situation.

3) Remember not to take things personally. This can be challenging in the beginning of your career. You want to be the best doula, and see your clients bloom and blossom. You may offer suggestions or provide information, and your client chooses something you consider to not be the best choice. You may question whether there was something else you might have said. It's best to remain neutral and know that when you provide all the services and information within your scope and agreement, you have done the best job possible. All choices are a reflection of who your client is, and what they feel is best for themselves and their family. When you internalize the things that go wrong or any constructive criticism, it becomes an energetic drain. There are so many emotions running high with a new mother, as well as family members -- all adjusting to a whole new world.

4) Understand the birth process. Postpartum, or the fourth trimester, is the period after birth. The birth is over, so you might ask: Why do I need to know about birth? You will probably hear the birth story, and you'll experience those early days and weeks with your client. Pregnancy, labor, birth and the postpartum period encompass the childbearing year. It is a complete cycle. We can't separate the birth from what comes next. Everything affects the early parenting experience. How a woman is treated during birth, intervention, how the baby is treated, the physical aftermath with any trauma, and how this mother was parented will all play a role in what happens next. Learn all you can about birth, particularly in your geographic area -- the providers, the places of birth, and the classes women and partners are enrolled in. The more you know, the better you can provide the support needed.

5) Leave your judge at home. Choices others make may not be the ones we make. When you can serve without judgment, you are meeting people where they are. This doesn't mean you withhold information, or don't speak up if you feel the mother's or baby's safety is in question. You will present all you know, and the choices are then up to the family. Check in with yourself if you find you are being judgmental. As humans, we rely on judgement to discern information and to stay safe. However, as a postpartum doula, the judgment about different lifestyles and choices will interfere in your service to others. It's a great idea to think about situations where you might be uncomfortable and your judge might come out. Perhaps, there is another doula that would be better suited for this family.

6) Practice listening. Remember, this is about your client and not you. Listen with an open heart. You do not need to share everything that happened to you or relate your story. When appropriate, and helpful to the situation, share some of your story. Avoid making it about you. When you really listen, you know what your role is with this mother and family, and you can be the best support for them during this time of transition. You will gain trust, and show empathy. Listen to the birth story of this mother, listen to the Dad, and be the space for them to embrace their new roles.

7) Offer all the facts and theories. Sometimes you know something to be true, yet you see your client doing something opposite. It isn't your job to change somebody's mind, but it is a disservice to withhold information that could result in a different choice. One of your jobs is to present the facts. At the same time, you have to take into consideration the person you are working with, and honor their uniqueness. Offer up what you know, or have seen work in other instances, and share resources. You will feel satisfied knowing that you have put forth all you can, and your client gets to make an informed choice.

8) Encourage rest and nutrition. This is the key to recovery, especially if the birth was traumatic or wrought with intervention. Rest and nutrition heal. These are two recommendations within your scope. There is such a thing as postpartum nutritional depletion. Certain foods are better than others. You can make it a point to learn about it. The only advice I ever really give is to sleep when the baby sleeps. That's easier said than done for many new mothers. You can prepare simple meals while you're working, and you can prepare other meals for later. You can encourage your client to explore sleep options and arrangements that will maximize sleep for the entire family. Learn about normal newborn sleep, and share that information with the families you serve. This will support your effort to encourage realistic expectations about sleep.

9) Set boundaries. This is crucial so you don't burn out. You want to be available, and responsive to your clients. Does this mean you answer calls and are available 24/7? It is your choice, and not a requirement. Postpartum doula work is designed to be a part time flexible service, to fill in the gaps with practical support and information. You can schedule your time according to your availability and the needs of the family. New mothers may be somewhat on their own, or they might also rely on friends and family for support. It does take a village, and you are not the entire village. If you are the sole source of support, you still have the choice to set your phone hours and your working hours. Only you know what will keep you in the game serving families.

10) Be an example. You are encouraging rest and nutrition. Do the same for yourself. You are encouraging families to bond. Be sure to not leave your family out as you serve other families. If you are sharing about attachment, have a sling to use and show.

If you are supporting a family with a toddler, show Mom ways to incorporate him into the newborn scene. Be professional, yet warm and open. New mothers need you to show them that it does get easier and they are not supposed to do it alone. Encouraging words and affirmations also go a long way.

BONUS: Work yourself out of a job. When you begin to work with a family, think about all you get to do to end your service. YES. This is very different from most jobs. Postpartum doulas are temporary. You are like Mary Poppins. Fly in, do what you do, then fly out and move on. You will have accomplished your mission, whether or not you feel the family is on a path you say is right or good. What you say and do could impact them later, even if you don't see the fruits of your labor at the time.

Most of all, find and bring the joy. Being a postpartum doula is an amazing journey of self-discovery as much as it is learning about motherhood, families and breastfeeding. Like anything in life, the giving is in the receiving and the receiving is in the giving. Be authentically you, and be open to learning all along the way. Shine your light. You will make a difference in the lives of the families you serve.

I'll share a story that will help you make sense of this bonus tip. I had a client that had extreme engorgement when I showed up on day one. After several phone calls, we were able to get a pump. Before the pump arrived, we got quite intimate. I massaged one breast while she did the other. She was in a lot of pain.

We managed to ease the discomfort and get the baby latched. It was hours into this process. We got close quickly. The gratitude for my services was expressed on a deep level. I served this family for about six weeks -- helping with breastfeeding, providing information, doing laundry and other chores.

One day when I walked in, my client was doing laundry. I started to fold. She said, "You sit down. What can I get you for breakfast?" I knew my time was up. There was a complete role reversal. It didn't feel right for my client to be waiting on me.

Trust me when I say: "You'll know when your time is up with a client."

Chapter 8 - Meeting Potential Clients

Before you begin this journey or set an appointment with anyone, it is a good idea to get to know your own philosophies regarding birth and parenting.

Give some thought to the following circumstances, and **feel** your gut reaction. Ask yourself if you could provide **non-judgmental support** in each situation.

There are so many environments and personalities you will encounter as you work with families. This, although it makes your job interesting, also reveals a lot about yourself. A postpartum doula steps into somebody else's home on their turf. It's your job to guide, educate, listen and support.

Here is a list, certainly not exhaustive, of various situations you might encounter:

smoking in the home
formula feeding
gay couples
transgender couples
teen parents
junk food junkies
spanking of other children
guns in the house
drug use
attachment parenting (or the opposite -- baby-wise parenting)
many wild pets
single mother who purchased sperm to get pregnant

There are many questions you can ask ahead on the phone to know whether you are a good fit for somebody. If you are allergic to cats, you should ask about pets up front -- save yourself a trip if you find out this potential client has a cat or two.

If a client calls, seeking your service months or weeks in advance of giving birth, you have an opportunity to meet with these families to learn more about their vision and expectations for the postpartum period. I believe it's a good idea to meet them in their home so you can get a feel for the environment you'll be working in. This is a two-way interview. Not only is the family gathering information about your experience, training and philosophy, but you are also gathering information about prospective clients.

This is the time to decide if you are the right doula for the job. Your experience and wisdom are valuable no matter what stage you're at in your doula career. However, you and the family need to feel a connection, and be able to establish a rapport. This connection is just as important as experience, in guiding families in their hiring process.

In Chapter 15 you'll find my *Client Intake Form* and my *Fourth Trimester Vision.* Remember to use some type of screening tool on the phone so you can decide whether it makes sense to go further. If you've already determined your ideal client or target market, this will be much easier. You'll know exactly who you want to work with. Once hired, you can use the Vision form to find out more about your client's anticipated needs.

Chapter 9 - Educating Clients And Yourself

This has become quite controversial lately. It really isn't the responsibility of the postpartum doula to educate clients about everything. That doesn't mean we don't need to be educated. We need to know about basic non-medical care in the fourth trimester. We also need to know who to call or to whom we refer, when we don't know the answer. The main thing is to recognize your own limitations, and be resourceful.

With that in mind, do the self-assessment to see where you're starting. Look these things up if you aren't sure. This is what you'll do if you're asked a question from your client, and the answer doesn't roll off your tongue. Try not to get caught up in the "I don't know enough to get started" syndrome. There will always be more to learn.

How Do I Teach and How Do I Learn?

There are many topics you can become well versed on. Decide which topics you need to learn more about and how you'll learn about them. These are some topics to consider:

1) Bonding and attachment

2) Postpartum emotional reactions

3) Physical changes that occur after birth

4) Latch-on and positioning at the breast

5) Breastfeeding and returning to work

6) Newborn characteristics and development

How would you educate your clients if asked about something? Share what you know is true, or has helped other women and families. Guide them toward reliable, evidence-based sources: this could be a specific video, book, journal, article, website, pamphlet, community resource, or class.

What Do I Know?

While you do this self-assessment, try not to think too hard about the answer. Respond with what comes to your mind first. Give a lot of thought to where your answers are coming from. **Our views can be rooted in anything: facts, opinions, values, or old wives tales.** Develop a practice of asking yourself: Is your answer the right one for all your clients? Is it factually true?

True or False

1. Baby Blues are experienced by a majority of women in the U.S.
2. A new baby should not be in public for at least a month.
3. Formula-fed babies need to be on a feeding schedule.
4. If you hold a baby too much, you can spoil them.
5. A newborn needs to cry to develop their lungs.
6. Breastfeeding babies should never have a pacifier.
7. If a newborn has jaundice, they should always be hospitalized.
8. A mother should not eat spicy foods when nursing

9. If a baby is 9lbs. or more at birth, they will need formula supplements if nursing.

10. A lack of touch in infancy has been linked to relationship problems later in life.

11. Crying babies are heard more in the United States than in other countries.

12. Moms should never take meds while nursing.

13. Breastfeeding your newborn lowers their risk of SIDS.

14. A newborn can imitate facial expressions.

15. Massage and touch can save a baby's life.

Multiple Choice

16. The safest place for a baby to sleep is

a) with their parents
b) in a bassinet
c) in a crib
d) in a co-sleeper
e) other

17. The safest place for a baby to be born is

a) home
b) hospital
c) birth center

18. Research indicates that the best time for parents to interact playfully with their babies is

a) after nap time
b) in the quiet alert state
c) in the active alert state
d) after feeding

19. The worldwide weaning age (in years) is about

a) 2 ½
b) 3
c) 3 ½
d) 4 ½

20. Babies most like to look at

a) black and white patterns
b) human faces
c) colorful shapes
d) colorful patterns

21. The number one predictor of successful breastfeeding is

a) a mother's desire
b) support
c) a mother's commitment
d) breastfeeding within the first hour of life

22. When a baby has colic, it is due to

a) a gastrointestinal problem
b) a nervous mother
c) reflux
d) unknown causes

23. When do babies develop a temperament?

a) at two weeks
b) at two months
c) at two years
d) they are born with it

24. Approximately how long does it take for a baby to adjust to life outside the womb?

a) two weeks

b) two months
c) four weeks
d) three months

Think about these questions and how you would answer them if asked by a new mother or expectant parent. They will come up over and over again. It's a good idea to know the answer, and more important to know *how* you answer, and where your answer is coming from.

Maybe asking the question right back is all you need to do. Or asking another question to find out why they're asking in the first place. Often there's an underlying reason for the question. For example, if someone is asking about pacifier use, perhaps they need some support with breastfeeding. Remember that a "should" question is not one for you to answer. It's not for you to decide.

Check out these frequently asked questions and consider whether or not you have an answer. And, how you would answer these.

Common FAQs From New Mothers

1. Should I sleep with my baby?
2. Can I supplement breastfeeding with formula?
3. How often should I bathe my baby?
4. Should I use a pacifier?
5. Should I immunize my baby?

Breastfeeding FAQs

1. Should I stay away from certain foods?
2. Do I breastfeed each time my baby cries?
3. How long should I nurse on each side?
4. My baby is very sleepy at the breast, what should I do?
5. How do I know I have enough milk?

Chapter 10 - Learn About Childbirth

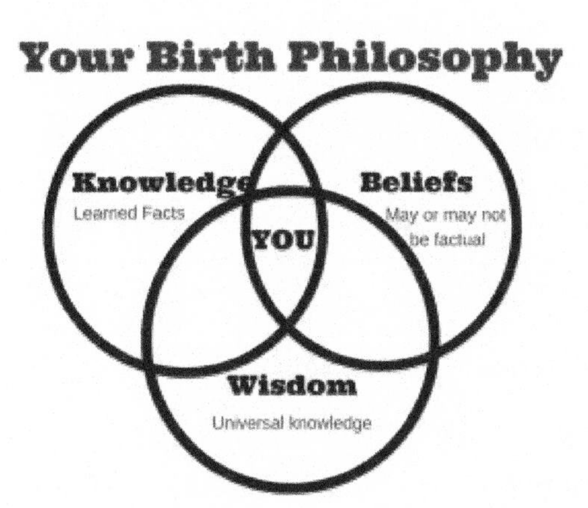

What is Your Birth Philosophy?

These are some questions I developed to get you thinking about what you already know about birth, and what you believe. Postpartum doulas need to know about the process, and the trends in maternity care, as well as what happened during their client's birth.

There is no right or wrong. Write down all of your thoughts and feelings and elaborate on your vision for your birth (real or imagined). You can draw your vision, or even create a vision board with old magazines, scissors and glue. See where it takes you.

What you believe will reflect back to you while working with clients.

1) Birth is:

a. a normal physiological process (midwifery model of care)

b. an event that requires medical intervention and management (medical model of care)

2) My greatest fear about birth is:

a. none
b. caesarean section
c. pain
d. negative effects on my body or my partner's body
e. something wrong with baby
f. other ______________________

3) I usually relax by:
a. listening to music
b. meditating
c. drinking alcohol
d. watching TV
e. other ______________________
f. I don't know how to relax

4) When I have pain, I:
a. take a pill
b. pay no attention
c. focus on it
d. go to the doctor
e. look up symptoms online
f. other _________________________

5) I trust my body's ability to give birth
a. yes
b. no

6) The safest place to give birth is:
a. home
b. hospital
c. birth center

7) Generally, when I go to the doctor I:
a. trust everything he/she tells me
b. have a lot of questions
c. research on my own
d. go for a second opinion
e. I don't go to the doctor

f. other ____________________

8) I believe:

a. the doctor or midwife delivers the baby
b. women give birth to their baby

How do you feel after taking some time to answer these questions? I bet you have more questions. Maybe you discovered how much you already know about your beliefs about birth. You may feel like you have a lot to learn. Remember that your answers will not necessarily match up with your client's answers. The key is to know what you believe, and to know that your clients may have very different beliefs.

Ask yourself, "Can I serve without judgment?"

Even though you're serving families after birth, you could be asked many questions that clients have about birth. What are the trends in your community? Who are the prenatal care providers? What are women and families reading and hearing about birth?

There are two very distinct models of care: the midwifery model and the medical model. The midwifery model says that birth is a normal event, and requires holistic care, and a hands off approach. The medical model says birth is an illness and needs management and intervention.

Because the medical model still prevails, there are many things women are either told or that they learn as young girls, that are not necessarily true. These things have become cultural beliefs that have taken power away from birthing women.

What follows is a list that I made, from what I've learned and experienced over the years. Feel free to share this with your clients.

Top 10 Lies Women Have Been Sold About Childbirth

1) Pregnancy is an illness.

Most women (in the U.S.) give birth in the hospital. Hospitals are for sick people. People with disease and illness, emergencies, tests, and procedures. Because this is what hospitals were designed for, pregnant women will be treated as such. You may not be told you are ill when you are pregnant, but the messages you receive in our culture tell you so. The treatment and care within the medical establishment create this experience by design.

2) Birth requires intervention and management.

The majority of women use epidural for pain relief. This requires lots of other interventions, including I.V., Electronic Fetal Monitoring, blood pressure checks, and more. Induction is rampant. The use of artificial oxytocin (Pitocin) also requires many interventions and a lot of times leads to a woman's request for epidural. You've likely been told that epidural is the best pain relief method and there are no risks. You can read and research about the benefits and risks. What about the risk of all the other interventions that come with the epidural, or the induction, or both?

3) The hospital is the safest place to give birth.

It is all really relative to the particular hospital you choose to give birth in. The Leap Frog group has graded hospitals. Where does yours land? In addition, there are many germs to be found in a hospital. The management of labor in a medical setting often leads to interventions that slow or stop labor. Interventions may also create the scenario whereby the baby's heart rate drops, Mom's blood pressure drops, or both. This then could lead to a cesarean section, which is major abdominal surgery. There are risks associated with surgery -- your body cavity is open and anything is possible. The hospital can be a safe place, but I would question whether it is "the safest" place. Where do you feel safe?

4) You require many tests and procedures during pregnancy.

Glucose test, GBS test, blood tests, pee test, non-stress test, vaginal exams. There are more. Do you require all of these to be safe and healthy? I'm not saying yes or no. I'm saying that not everyone needs everything. You may have your unique set of risk factors. And it is not necessarily the same as it is for your friend. My point is that you get to be educated on what these are and you get to choose. There is no one-size-fits-all, as you may have experienced, or are about to. Check out the B.R.A.I. N. S. model of decision-making.

5) Birth is an event to fear.

This is the perception that seems to have taken over in childbirth. Fear will stop, stall, or prevent labor. What you believe will show up in your experience. I know hundreds of women who have had the most amazing birth experience you can imagine. Of course, it is normal and common to have a fear of the unknown. Irrational and chronic fear wreaks havoc on your body. You hear horror stories, maybe you watch some intense TV show that gives you a horrible image.

Conversely, birth is a rite of passage -- a transformational event in a woman's life that will help her find her power. Birth can be joyful, and even orgasmic for some women. It is not separate from your life and how you live it. Do you want to fear birth -- or learn about it, face your fears, and trust the process?

6) Epidural is the best method of pain relief.

If you believe it is the best method, then so it is. Pain is a perception. At one point in history, women were demanding pain relief during birth. They thought they deserved it. Then there became a demand for natural birth, when women realized they had no recall of their experience, and were not in control. I believe all options must be available. And, that women deserve the truth about all benefits and risks. Not every epidural provides maximum pain relief. Some don't take all the way. Some wear off quickly. Some are given too early in labor. As Marshall Klauss once said, "If a doula were a drug it would be unethical not to offer it." Doulas can give you the confidence to birth your baby by being with you every step of the way. There are many methods of non-drug pain relief, including hypnobirthing, acupuncture, Reiki, and massage.

7) Your baby has a due date.

You are given an EDD, estimated date of delivery. **ESTIMATED!**

There is no exact date. There is a two week window of time on either end of this date. It's important for you to remember this when you are tired in your ninth month of pregnancy. It is tempting to be induced, depending on what you are being told. Your baby is big, your pelvis is small, or your fluid is low. You might want to schedule a C-section. I have heard these things from other women. Before you opt for an induction or a scheduled C-section, find out if your baby is okay. Ask about a non-stress test. If your baby is okay, what is the rush?

8) Drugs in labor don't affect your baby.

This is not always true. It depends which drug, how much, and when. A sleepy baby could be still feeling the effects of drugs given during labor. If you've ever seen the breast crawl video, the evidence is overwhelming. The babies that were from non-medicated births crawled to the breast. Babies in the medicated group sometimes figure it out, but not right away. Educate yourself on what the drug options are. Know what is being given to you, if this is what you choose. More long term studies are needed to determine what happens to a baby that has been exposed to some of these drugs.

9) Your cervix must be checked for dilation.

You can say yes or no to this. Your cervix will ripen and open when your baby is ready, and your body is ready. Birth is not an exact science. You can be one or two centimeters dilated for weeks. Or you could go into active labor very quickly. Your body is your guide to what is happening. I know many women who have been told that it would be a while, then boom. These women knew their bodies were ready. The baby is born just an hour or two later. I've also heard many women share frustration of being one or two centimeters dilated and nothing is happening. Being checked for dilation can excite you or discourage you. It depends what you hear from the person checking the cervix. Risk of infection increases with more hands inside your vagina.

10) Routine ultrasound is 100 percent safe.

There are several studies that point to the fact that the research isn't clear. You can easily find out what ultrasound is, and what it does to the cells. When something is done routinely, it doesn't necessarily mean it is 100 percent safe. We do know that the American College of Obstetricians and Gynecologists (ACOG) and other groups do not recommend routine ultrasound for a non-medical reason. Also, a big baby diagnosis from an ultrasound later in pregnancy can be off by 1-2 pounds. **ACOG never recommends the 3-D and 4-D ultrasounds, which are usually performed by untrained people.**

I understand that most women and families today want to know their baby's sex. Though, I would say that the element of surprise is like no other. I'm pointing out that we could be finding out years from now (when the research catches up to the practice), that all these ultrasounds have done some damage.

Chapter 11 - Perinatal Mood And Anxiety Disorders (Pmads)

Perinatal mood and anxiety disorders (PMADs) affect one in seven or more women during pregnancy, or after birth. It is the **most common complication of childbirth**. Sadly, there is still a lack of well-trained and knowledgeable caregivers to address this complication.

As a postpartum doula, it is wise to be well-versed on symptoms that may present with a client. You may or may not know their history. You can learn what these mood disorders are, and what you might observe. This is a synopsis.

A quality training will cover this in more depth, and there are many other trainings that go into more details. Postpartum Support International (PSI) is one of the most well-known organizations that offer both training for the professional, and support and resources for women and families.

Always recommend a referral when any of these symptoms are present. You are not a counselor, social worker, or an expert on handling mental health. If you do have one of these licenses or certifications, make it known to your clients, and use those skills accordingly.

Mood Disorders – Quick Reference

Baby Blues – Marked by crying, irritability, and fatigue, baby blues is very common. In fact, about 60-80% of all new mothers experience the blues. It can be overwhelming to become a new mother, yet mothers who experience the blues are predominantly happy. If the blues last more than a few days to two weeks, then it could be something more. Watch for severity, timing and duration.

Depression, Anxiety, Panic – Because these disorders are often co-mingled, they fall into one category. Depressive symptoms look similar to the blues with the crying, fatigue, and irritability. But with depression, there can be severe sleep disturbances, appetite changes, anger, lack of bonding, and hopelessness. With anxiety, you can add constant worry, shortness of breath and heart palpitations to the list of depressive symptoms. Panic attacks involve extreme anxiety, with possible dizziness and rapid heart rate. Panic involves the fear of losing control, or fear of dying or going crazy. All of these interfere with bonding. **If a mother is not feeling like herself more often than not, there is likely a problem.**

Post-Traumatic Stress Disorder (PTSD) – This involves reliving a traumatic event. In the case with new mothers the event is the birth, or it could be something from their own childhood experience. This is a birth where they felt out of control, they were fearful during the process, and they may be blaming others for what happened. This trauma plays a role in future pregnancies and births, possible sexual dysfunction and a lack of bonding with baby. If it is something from the distant past, there may be a lot to unpack.

Obsessive Compulsive Disorder (OCD) – This could also occur with depression. Women can have scary thoughts about their baby. These women are fearful of the repetitive intrusive thoughts they are having and are afraid to speak up. They do not act on these thoughts. Often, they go overboard to avoid harming their baby. They may check their baby much more than is necessary out of fear that something is wrong. There is an obsession with order and cleanliness.

Bipolar Disorder (I and II) – With Bipolar I there are alternating periods of depression and elevated mood. This is noticed by others and is not simply a sad or happy Mom. Oftentimes, the elevated mood, or mania as it is called, requires hospitalization. The depressive symptoms of Bipolar II are severe. This disorder is often misdiagnosed as depression. The mania is marked by distinct periods of grandiosity, racing thoughts and less need for sleep. Bipolar disorder is a chronic condition.

Psychosis – A majority of women who have psychosis meet the criteria for bipolar disorder. There is a history of psychotic episodes or a family history. This illness comes with delusions or hallucinations. There are rapid mood swings and there is confusion. Unlike with OCD, women with psychosis do not know the intrusive thoughts are unhealthy. Thoughts of harming the baby can easily lead to acting on those thoughts.

Note: This reference sheet is not meant as a complete guide to mood disorders, nor as a tool for diagnoses. It is meant for a quick glance and an overview of the differences and similarities between these illnesses. For more complete definitions and explanations, you are encouraged to participate in a full training on perinatal mood disorders.

Chapter 12 - Breastfeeding Support

Breastfeeding support is something you will do a lot of as a postpartum doula. I remember when I first started this work, and I had to take a breastfeeding class as part of my training. I seriously thought it was the craziest thing. My only experience to that point was breastfeeding my first born son, Matthew.

I remember being in the hospital, in bed, and I was struggling a bit with the latch. A friend, who used to babysit me (we were ten years apart), made a couple of suggestions and helped me position. Voila! It worked. I never had any problems. It was super easy from that point on.

When I had to take a class, I thought, "It isn't that complicated. What is there to know?"

Two dehydrated babies and cracked nipples presented themselves in the early months on the job. I certainly learned a lot about what could go wrong with breastfeeding. I learned more and more as time went on.

Support is the secret to success with breastfeeding. The women of the village that breastfed are not always available, nor are they all breastfeeding. We still have a culture where breastfeeding is considered the best choice, and not everyone's cup of tea. I'll never understand the reasons why anybody chooses not to breastfeed, and I can still support them as a postpartum doula.

I don't have to understand this choice. If they choose to breastfeed, I will go the extra mile to ensure they don't quit. I've seen some mothers quit at the first sign of a challenge. I've witnessed an adoptive mother breastfeed with a supplemental feeding system. I've supported mothers who chose to pump only.

There's no comparison of breastmilk to formula. They're not in the same league. It's like comparing apples and pears. For those mothers that choose breastfeeding, I have created these ten strategies (there are more) you can use with everyone. There will be individualized needs as well.

Ten Ways to Support a Breastfeeding Mother

1) Encourage the breastfeeding mother to set up one or two areas in the house where she is comfortable breastfeeding. She could have a basket with snacks, phone and other items she wants nearby. There could be comfortable pillows and a good straight back chair. And you can show her how to comfortably and safely side lie nursing in bed. You can help her set this up.

2) Encourage nutrition. You can provide healthful snacks and meals while you are there with your client. You can also remind her to drink fluids like water, juice, and other liquids with little or no sugar and caffeine.

3) Suggest minimal company. Many mothers want to have family and friends over to celebrate the birth of their baby. They may not realize how exhausting this can be. When mothers are learning the rhythm of breastfeeding it is best to focus on their babies to learn their cues.

4) Guide the breastfeeding mother to recognize the baby's feeding cues, and general body language. Crying is a late signal. Share your knowledge with the new mother so she gets to know her baby, and recognizes when it is time to feed her baby, time to play, time to sleep or time to calm.

5) Pamper the breastfeeding mother. Offer a gentle massage of her shoulders. Bring her a meal in bed. Prepare her favorite meal or snack. Offer her an opportunity to take a nice long shower to relax while you listen for the baby awakening to breastfeed.

6) Check in with Mom. You can text or call in between your visits to find out what's happening. Always follow up when a new suggestion or routine is established with latch and positioning.

7) Watch, observe and support during a breastfeeding session. You have the knowledge to see a good latch, and know when to suggest other positions for a successful latch. This is the key for the mother to be confident in her breastfeeding. When baby is latching properly and getting enough milk, breastfeeding flows smoothly.

8) Introduce the breastfeeding mother to La Leche League or another breastfeeding support group. There is great value for her to be around other breastfeeding mothers and to be able to ask questions and share challenges and concerns.

9) Always have an IBCLC or a CLC on your resource list. When a challenge arises beyond a positioning and latch-on situation (or beyond your scope of knowledge), you will be able to make a referral to someone who has more experience and has had more training. Establish a rapport with this person, so you can send a quick text or make a call.

10) Share positive stories and successes of other mothers. This will inspire your client to continue breastfeeding knowing that she is not alone in any challenge she might encounter. Ensure her that she will do this, and that she is doing it.

Chapter 13 - Put On Your Business Hat

The Business of Being a Postpartum Doula

Let's talk about the business side of being a postpartum doula. This is another hat you may wear if you choose to go into business for yourself, or with somebody else. You can be really great at what you do -- and may or may not have ever run a business, or marketed yourself to others.

Here is what I know, and what I have learned over the years, that works.

1) Determine all the services you wish to offer.

Typically, postpartum doulas offer guidance (newborn behavior, breastfeeding, daily infant care), education and practical support (cooking, laundry, sibling care, errands), and resources. If you have other certifications or degrees that make you stand out, you can add that on.

For example, nutrition, herbs, massage, and Reiki. These are all additional services you can charge for. Be sure to make it known, and be current with your education and insurance (if required). Also, check with your certifying organization about what they have to say about other services.

2) Meet all the doulas, birth educators, home health workers, midwives, nurses, hospital and birth center staff, pediatricians, obstetricians, lactation professionals, and all others who are in touch with new and expectant families.

These contacts are what will drive your business. Personal connection is important. Social media is great and has its place. Nothing replaces true live connection in your own community.

- You can arrange a lunch or breakfast for staff (bringing it to docs works like a charm to get an appointment)
- Bring flyers or business cards for waiting rooms
- Offer to do a talk or educational session for clients or patients
- Ask educators about attending one of their classes to introduce yourself
- Attend health and baby fairs locally

Follow-up with all leads and new connections.

3) Create your own code of ethics.

Creating your own code entails choosing what you can support (and not support) in a non-judgmental way. You always want to support your client's choices, and offer all the information they are asking for.

However, it is important that you know where you stand with your own morals and values. Let this be one of your guides to accepting or not accepting a client. Many postpartum doulas take on any and all clients that call. Others only work with breastfeeding Moms. I do not recommend compromising your own values in an effort to support another.

In the beginning, you will have a much richer experience by serving many different families with varying lifestyles and choices. This will help you determine your code.

Most certifying organizations have a code of ethics you're expected to abide by.

4) Establish your rates and hours of work.

This is a question that comes up a lot. How much do I charge? How many hours do I work? Do I do nights? Only days? More for twins? Less for more hours purchased? Packages?

I recommend learning what the going rates are in your area. Use that as a guide. Let's hypothesize that New York City doulas charge roughly $50/hr. If you live in rural Alabama, that rate is probably out of sync with your local economy. Establish your own worth. Reflect on your experience and education to date. Take into account the expenses you will incur on the job such as travel, child care, copying materials, education, and anything else.

Unlike birth doulas, postpartum doulas can establish the hours they want to work. You can do days only, or nights only. You can combine. This is determined by when you want to work, and other obligations you have.

There is not a need to be on-call for weeks on end. You can ask your clients to let you know when their baby is born. Be sure you are on the call or text list. That way you have a day or two to plan. You can be on call if you want to be. There is nothing wrong with setting boundaries, with phone hours, texting, and communication.

Originally, postpartum doulas filled in the blanks. Three to five hours per day, maybe every day or a few days per week. It seems now that many mothers want more full-time help. Again, your choice. How much do you want to work? Are you a postpartum doula or a baby nurse?

Many doulas offer packages, with more hours equaling less per hour. Check out the doulas in your area, and elsewhere and determine what will work for you and the clients you are serving.

5) Choose your back-up.

This is critical. When you are expected to serve a new mother and family, it is your obligation to be there or replace yourself if needed. You don't want to put yourself in a position of being the only one, and then having your car break down, leaving a new mother stranded in a possible anxious state. Find someone you connect with -- another doula on the path -- that shares a similar philosophy and whom you can trust. Let your client meet this person and feel comfortable.

If you live in an area where there aren't any other doulas, or they are spread out, let your clients know this. You are paving the way for doulas. I got started this way. My mom was my back-up! There was no other postpartum doula, and no certification for postpartum doulas in the early 1990s.

Let your clients know you will be there no matter what, unless you have an emergency. When you are up front and honest from the beginning, you have established trust.

6) Protect yourself with a contract.

When I got started I shook hands with my clients. No contract. Once I got taken for money the first time (of a few times over the years), I wrote a contract. It doesn't have to be complicated, or lengthy. In all my years of being a doula, I have never heard of anybody being sued. I'm not saying that it hasn't happened or that it couldn't happen. What I am saying is I believe the contract can be simple.

I have an example in this section.

The contract does several things:

- Establishes agreed upon services
- Fully discloses rates
- Guarantees client you are available for them
- Gives you guaranteed income
- Allows you to say yes or no to other clients (similar due dates)
- Creates cash flow with deposits for future services

This doesn't mean you still can't be flexible. There are some postpartum doulas that will refund deposits if things shift dramatically for clients. Others keep the deposit, no matter what, as they state in their contract.

For example, the grandmother who could not come suddenly makes room on her calendar to be there for her daughter. The family now does not require your services. The problem is that you have cleared your calendar and refused other clients (losing income) to serve this family. What you do about it is your choice.

Another option is to take people to small claims court. I never have. The handful of times that people didn't pay was because of some dissatisfaction with services rendered, and they were small amounts of money. Again, it's your choice as to how far you want to go.

I view the contract more as a written handshake. Most people are hiring you for the support they anticipate needing, and are appreciative of your services. That is why clear expectations of the dos and don'ts are so important in the contract.

7) Screen clients on the telephone

This saves time for everyone. The key here is to ask the questions that help you determine whether you want to work for this client.

If you have pet allergies or are afraid of big dogs, ask your clients if they have pets. Be honest about your situation. Right away, you will want to refer if you are not fully equipped to deal with their pets.

My biggest lesson with this was when a client called last minute, and I sent a doula to work. There was smoking in the home, and no matter what the doula shared about the dangers, it didn't stop. The doula was also getting very sick from the smoke and I took her off the job.

After that, I always asked if there is smoking in the home.

Basically, this all goes back to your personal code of ethics, as well as your health and safety. You want to be clear that you offer non-judgmental support, but are protecting yourself as well.

8) Maintain an online presence

This is a given in today's world. Social media can be a huge learning curve, and can be as fun or as daunting as you make it. I recommend picking one or two platforms where you are comfortable, and where your target market hangs out.

Learn all you can about these platforms.

- What kinds of posts attract the most attention and conversation?

- Are you looking to create awareness, or are you asking people to take some action?
- What is the best time of day to post?
- Is there a scheduler that could help you organize?
- Do you want to hire someone to help you with this?
- How much time do you want to spend online vs. live connection?

Nothing beats a website. This is your storefront, where you can send people to go look, and learn more about you, your mission, and your business. From experience (beginning when websites could only be built with HTML coding), you will likely want to make periodic changes. Keep it simple, crisp, and easy to navigate. There are many easy templates and website builders. Ask others, and find one where you won't have to hire out for every fix and change. Create a budget for this.

9) Take a business class or find a S.C.O.R.E. mentor

If you have never run a business or have lots of questions about legalities, accounting, and business plans, find an online or local course. Connect with a business professional who does one on one, for strategy and support. You do not have to feel like you are on an island alone.

S.C.O.R.E. stands for Service Core of Retired Executives. Many community colleges house the S.C.O.R.E. office. Check out their website for more information. When you make an appointment, they will find you a mentor that best suits your needs. It is always FREE. Take advantage if this is available to you. They can help with a business plan, guide you to financing, and point you in the right direction. They may have free or inexpensive business classes.

You do not have to immediately become incorporated (LLC, S-Corp., C-Corp.). This will depend on your personal financial status and tax status. There are advantages to doing this, but it is not advantageous for everyone. Do check in with your accountant for advice.

When I started, I became a sole proprietor. This involves choosing a name, and filing it with the state or county where you reside. I picked the name Tenth Month Doula Services. Officially, I was Betsy K. Schwartz doing business as (DBA) Tenth Month Doula Services. This is a simple way to pick a business name, other than your own name. This worked for me in the beginning. I have since changed my business name to Birth in the Know, LLC.

10) Check in with your strategy and goals. Repeat often.

With any business, there will be times when something isn't working. Evaluate what you are doing with marketing, networking and social media. Find a way to track your time and effort so you know what makes sense to keep doing.

Technology changes so quickly, it can be difficult to keep up. Carve out some time for you to learn what's new, and to reformulate a plan.

Be sure your resources and referral contact information is up-to-date. You want to be giving your clients accurate information, and be referring to people that are still in business.

Focus on what is working, and change what isn't. You can do this every month, every few months, or twice a year. Just do it. Working on your business is different from working in your business.

Some of this process may involve self-reflection. Perhaps, you handled a specific situation in a way that you aren't feeling great about. When you are able to remove the judgment or negative self-talk, you can create a new strategy for the next time the same situation arises.

Know what your strengths are, and know when to reach out for support from someone who knows a little more than you do, in regard to things you are challenged by. It's a great way to connect with like-minded people, and also get the help you need.

Your business is **you!** It is about standing out, not fitting in. Embrace your own personal style, and share your big why with your clients. Come back to your why when you have moments of doubt or when things aren't clear.

It is most often when we step back from a challenge, question, or situation that the answers present themselves.

What to Include in a Marketing Strategy

Here are some ideas in business language that will get you thinking with your business hat on. They may not all apply to you now, but if your goal is to establish and run a business, you've got to think like a business owner. You can always get support with some of the tasks, once you have a roadmap. You will revisit this and revise your goals and strategies as often as you need.

Marketing Vision and Goals

It's so important to have a big vision. This will guide you in everything you do, and keep you moving forward even when you feel like giving up. There are moments when your business will fluctuate, and you'll need to adjust. Your vision might even change down the road. For now, get really clear on this so you know what you are committed to.

1) Personal considerations: Think about your overall vision for your life. What kind of income and lifestyle do you desire? Consider vacations, hours you want to work, family/work balance, recognition, classes you want to take, etc.

2) Business vision: How many clients will you need to serve? Will there be repeat clients? So much earned per client, or so much revenue per month?

3) What is your strategy? Do you want a certain market share or partners in your business? Is there a particular geographic area you want to serve?

4) What will you need to do from a tactical standpoint? Example: Create a website, hire a marketing consultant or social media specialist.

Marketing Purpose: What is the purpose for your company? Why does the world need your business?

Marketing Visual: How would an ideal client experience your service / business? What would they feel or how would they experience the service?

SWOT Analysis: Create Your Own

This is a great tool to do every 90 days. You can use this to evaluate people (maybe just you) in your organization (specifically on strengths and weaknesses) -- as well as for your business as a whole. Evaluate your business for its **S**trengths, **W**eaknesses, **O**pportunities and **T**hreats. Once that is complete, evaluate your strengths and weaknesses.

Company SWOT:

Strengths: Internal to your company

Weaknesses: Internal to your company

Opportunities: External

Threats: External

Personal SWOT:

Strengths:

Weaknesses:

Opportunities: External

Threats: External

Ideal Customer:

Who is your ideal customer or client?

How do you answer a frustration or need they may have?

What problem or challenge is your ideal customer looking to

solve or resolve?

How would you spot your ideal customer?

Remarkable Difference:

There may be lots of doula businesses near you and they may offer similar services. How will your business differentiate itself? If your ideal customer / client meets you or learns of your business, why will they choose you over another doula business? How will your services or products stand out? Is it the way you do business? The passion you have for the business?

Core Message:

Now that you know your remarkable difference, create a Core Message that quickly communicates your difference. You want to tell customers what they will enjoy when they purchase from you. This is about what benefits customers get from you and how they will feel when they use your services -- not your list of features. For example: when you hire xyz Doula Service you will feel nurtured and mothered, while you get to know your baby.

Product / Service Innovation:

What are the products or services that your company offers? Start with something you give away to entice further business. Below is an example of what it might look like.

- Suspects: Free seminar, workshop, PDF, newsletter etc. (sign up or opt-in on website)
- Prospects ($150 or less): Low cost group class, individual class, product, or consult
- Clients ($500-$2,500): Those that contract your services for a short term
- Premium Clients ($5,000-$25,000): Those that contract for an extended time
- Champions: Strategic Partners, or collaborators. People that promote the business (often former clients who write

testimonials).

Lead Generation:

How do you currently get or plan to get clients? Are there ways that you have not thought of to get clients, but feel it would be good to try? Below are some examples.

- Social media activity
- Advertising
- Baby fairs and events
- Affiliate or Referral Plan

How do you track your leads? (i.e. Google Analytics)

Lead Conversion:

What is your system for following up with prospects?
How do you educate your prospects until they become clients?

Service Experience:

Once you have clients / customers, the goal is to keep them coming back for other things you offer -- or, have them generate new business for you through referrals.

Think about what to do to "wow" your clients. Are there surprises built into your products / services?

Do you do any client-only special events?

Consider how you might do one or some of these things:

- Customer-only events
- Handwritten thank you notes
- Satisfaction/referral surveys
- Results reviews

Critical Numbers:

How will you track your expenses including:

- Sales and cost of sales
- Marketing expenses
- Leads generated
- Leads converted
- Copying/printing

- Travel
- Education

How will you be held accountable in keeping track of the numbers? Of achieving your marketing strategies? Following up with prospects? Perhaps consider a business accountability buddy. You might want to hire a business coach, someone familiar with the doula business.

Marketing Expense Budget:

When spending money on marketing, your goal is a return on investment (ROI). Creating a well thought out strategy with a budget in mind is the key. You can always change course if it isn't working. You want to be tracking the money spent, and measuring your ROI.

- What is your total expense budget?
- Do you have a timeline to increase (or decrease) your sales and marketing expenditures? Why?
- Do your marketing expenses reflect your marketing strategies for lead generation, conversion, and moving prospects through to become clients?
- What percent of sales are you planning to spend on expenses? Is that level appropriate for your marketing strategy?

I know that was a lot to digest, and you may be feeling uncomfortable or overwhelmed. Use what you want from this marketing strategy. Sit down and really think about these things because it will help you in the long game.

Honestly, when I first started out, I didn't do any of this. There was no such thing as the Internet, and there were no other doula services. It was a lot easier in many ways. Nowadays, you may have some competition, but really that means that doulas are more well-known. You still bring your unique self to this work. There is always a way to do it, and you can be as creative and innovative as you choose to be.

Maybe you'll go to work for an established agency, and not even start your own business. And you might find that working for someone else isn't what you want to do for long. Either way, you have a framework to begin wearing your business hat.

Business Tips And Forms

Marketing Essentials

1. Put your name and contact information on everything (telephone, website).
2. Use logo and color combinations that feel good to you.
3. When networking, go to where your niche market is. In the beginning of your career, this may be very pregnant woman. Let the community know what services you offer. Many doulas specialize, for example, in working with twins.
4. It is not who you know, it's who knows you. The more people see your name in more places, the more credibility you'll have. People do business with people they know.
5. Develop an elevator speech -- explain yourself in ten to thirty seconds. For example, a postpartum doula takes the place of a mother or sister who can't be there to help out after birth.
6. Find and be a part of health fairs in your community. Many of these events are completely devoted to birth. These become annual events where you are gaining maximum exposure in your niche market.
7. Learn to use social media and then use it. Choose one or two platforms that you are comfortable with, and learn all you can about how you can leverage them. Then learn other platforms if you want. Be consistent.

8. Develop a website. There are many free tools available. You do not need to pay mega bucks to have this done. Be sure to choose a program that is user friendly. Hosting your site may be a minimum expense, though there are some free places. Do your research.
9. When you introduce yourself to a potential referral source, follow up and stay in touch. Bringing food adds a nice touch and they tend to remember you and look forward to seeing you again.
10. In developing your business cards and flyers, less is more. Don't crowd it. Fill it with just enough information to create a desire for the reader to call you for more information.
11. Create an enticing referral incentive for other doulas, clients and referral sources. This could be monetary, a gift or a barter.
12. Treat your services as a business, whether you set up your own or work for somebody. Consult a tax professional for the right fit for you.
13. Join other childbirth professional organizations and local organizations such as Chamber of Commerce and women's networking groups. Network with a mission of attracting customers from your niche market.

Chapter 14 - Activities

I've included these activities to get your juices flowing. This is a sampling of what you might encounter as a postpartum doula. A quality training will have a variety of role-plays and scenarios so you can practice ahead of time. Think about what you would say or do in each situation. The first activity is about thinking on your feet, reacting or not. It's more about getting to know you than solving the problem, or figuring out what to do. What does your gut say?

What Would I Do If?

I felt uncomfortable about the lack of discipline enforced in a client's home?

I found a bag of marijuana in the kitchen drawer of a client's home?

My client's husband greeted me at the door each night with a glass of wine in hand and wanted me to sit and chat?

My child was sick and I couldn't make it to my client's house that day?

A client called me in desperate need of help due to postpartum depression and she had no money to pay for my services?

If I heard there was a postpartum doula who was encouraging formula feeding?

If I suspected my client was being abused by her spouse?

This other activity is about you knowing your scope of practice, and having an up-to-date resource list. You'll want to be clear on when something is beyond what you are equipped to handle. We all don't know much more than we do know.

Educate, Nurture Or Refer

Is it time for education, comfort or referral? If education, what type? If comfort, how? If referral, to whom?

1. Your client is complaining of cesarean incision pain and discomfort and she
asks you to look at her stitches.

2. Your client tells you that her husband is having an affair and she doesn't know
what to do. Her family lives far away.

3. Your client shares with you that she is frightened by the amount of sweating she

is doing every night.

4. Your client is bleeding quite heavily at two weeks postpartum. She shares with
you that she has been doing lots of laundry and cleaning out her daughter's
closet.

5. Your client shares with you that her hemorrhoids are really bothering her and
she asks you what she can do to alleviate her discomfort.

6. Your client is breastfeeding but is having some difficulty due to her cesarean
incision.

7. Your breastfeeding client is severely engorged and she shares with you that she
has a slight fever and the chills.

8. Your client has cracked and bleeding nipples due to improper latch-on for the
first several days after birth.

9. You have a client who would like you to advise her on the use of acidophilus to
treat a yeast infection.

10. Your client is having trouble walking and sitting due to discomfort from
episiotomy.

11. Your client is complaining of lower back pain, likely a side effect of the epidural.

12. Your client has been very weepy almost every day and has indicated she has had trouble sleeping at night.

13. Your client is single and is emotionally torn about going back to work at six weeks.

14. Your client has very swollen ankles and wants to know what to do about it.

15. Your client is afraid to use the bathroom and has not moved her bowels in five days.

Chapter 15 - Sample Business Documents

Client Prenatal Intake (phone or in person)

Name
Due DateAddres
City ___________________ ZIP _________
Tel. #___________________ Cell # ____________Email: _____________

1. Where are you giving birth?

2. Who is your care provider?

3. Is this your first baby?

4. If not, how many siblings are there? What are their ages?

5. Do you have any recent experience with newborns?

6. Have you ever experienced any postpartum mood disorder (PMAD)? Do you or anybody in your family have a history of depression or mental health disorders?

7. Which feeding method do you plan to use?
Breastfeeding_____ Formula_____Undecided____

8. Have you chosen a pediatrician? If so, who is it?

9. Do you need more information on any of the following?
labor support parenting styles breastfeeding
yes___ no___ yes ___ no ___ yes___ no ___

emotional adjustment after birth child care parenting classes
yes ___ no ___ yes___ no___ yes ___ no ___

baby and me classes postpartum exercise
yes ___ no ___ yes ___ no ___

10. Is there any smoking in your home?

11. Do you have any pets? Please list.

12. Are you planning to go to work after you have your baby?

13. Do you have any worries or fears you would like to discuss?

14. What else should we be aware of?

A note to the doula: Use this as a guide. Feel free to add or delete or edit in any way that suits you. You may be able to ask some of these questions on the telephone to help you decide if this is a match for you.

Fourth Trimester Vision (once you're hired)

Some women prepare a birth plan or a vision for labor and birth. This can be done for the postpartum period, as well. Take the time to think about your postpartum needs. The postpartum period is a time of great upheaval and major transition for families. By making a plan or developing a vision ahead of the birth you may be better able to take care of yourself. This will also give your doula or other support person a guide for helping you take care of yourself and your home.

SUPPORT PEOPLE (Friends, Relatives, Doula)

Make a list of who will be available for support and what they can do to help; laundry, errands, sibling care, meal preparation, baby care, breastfeeding information and support.

Name	Help with
1) ______________	__________________________
2) ______________	__________________________
3) ______________	__________________________
4) ______________	__________________________

Write down at least one neighbor with a car who you could call in an emergency.

Make a list of all the important names and telephone numbers you and your support team will need. Place this list by the telephone.

Police ______________ Fire ______________
Pediatrician ______________
Doctor/midwife______________
Poison control______________
Husband/Partner-work ______________
Husband/Partner-cell____________
Mother______________
Mother-in-law______________

Neighbor_______________
Friend _______________

EATING HABITS

Special Needs

__Vegetarian __Vegan__Kosher__Diabetic__Low Sodium

List any food allergies.

Please name your favorite foods for each meal.

Breakfast

Lunch

Dinner

Snacks

LAUNDRY

Please write about the specific way you like your laundry done. Let your support people know if you use cold or hot water, fabric softener, and how you separate your laundry.

BABY'S SIBLINGS

Name Age

Favorite things to do

What we need to know

OTHER

List any medical problems you have and/or medications you are taking.

Please let us know about pets, any special care for them, or concerns.

List three things you could do to relax for 15 minutes per day.

1)____

2)____

3)____

Are you planning to work outside the home after the baby is born? If so, when would you start?

Will you need to start looking for suitable child care?

Do you need a breast pump and/or more information on working while breastfeeding?

Do you have any other special concerns?

Use the following as a beginning template for your contract. Add other services, and clauses that work for your doula business. Change your minimum hours requirement and deposit amount. You might want to figure out what your minimum shift requirement is, and your hourly rate or packages before creating a contract. This one was not reviewed by an attorney. That's something you might consider when you create yours.

Birth In The Know
Postpartum Doula Services Agreement

This agreement between Birth in the Know and of (city), requires a minimum of fifteen hours of postpartum caregiver services, to be rendered by a Birth in the Know Doula, within a two-week period. Additional hours may be purchased.

Services include the following non-medical support: basic guidance with breastfeeding and baby care, emotional support, household chores, meal preparation, errands, and sibling care. Any medical questions should be referred to an appropriate provider.

Opinions and recommendations of individual caregivers are solely that of the caregiver, and are not meant to be the advice or recommendation of Birth in the Know. **The client is solely responsible for final decisions in all aspects of care regarding herself and her baby.**

All fees, including applicable travel fees, shall be paid to the Doula on the last day of each work week. It is the responsibility of the client to mail any unpaid balance to Birth in the Know, P.O. Box 641114, Beverly Hills, FL 34464. An invoice shall be furnished by Birth in the Know for the client's financial records.

A $200.00 deposit shall be paid by said client in advance of services, or on the day services begin. This deposit is non-refundable should client cancel services prior to start.

$200.00 deposit enclosed yes no

Client signature Date

Birth in the Know Signature Date

Birth In The Know Service Evaluation

In order to better serve our clients, and respond to their needs, please take a few minutes to fill out this evaluation, and mail it in the self-addressed stamped envelope provided.

1.a. Where did you give birth?
b. Who was the attending midwife or obstetrician?

2. How did you find out about Birth in the Know?
   Were you referred? yes_ no_ If yes, by whom?
   Did you respond to an ad online? Yes __no__Where?
   Where did you pick up a brochure?

Your rating of our services (please circle):

1. Did our doula arrive promptly?

   a. always c. seldom
   b. most of the time d. not at all

2. Did you and your family feel comfortable with the presence of our doula?

   a. always c. seldom
   b. most of the time d. not at all

3. Did our doula seem knowledgeable regarding the care of your infant?

   a. always c. seldom
   b. most of the time d. not applicable

4. Did our doula seem knowledgeable regarding breastfeeding?

   a. always c. seldom
   b. most of the time d. not applicable

5. Which service(s) were most helpful to you and your family?

   a. household chores d. breastfeeding support

b. shopping and errands e. baby care guidance
c. sibling care f. meal preparation

6. Overall, how would you rate the quality of services you received from Birth in the Know?

a. excellent d. fair
b. very good e. poor
c. good

Comments:

May a potential client call you for a Birth in the Know reference? yes__ no__

Thank you for taking the time to help us serve our clients the best we can. Don't forget to tell pregnant friends and relatives about our services. Birth in the Know services are a wonderful gift!

Your name: (optional) Doula's name:

Chapter 16 - Resources And Definitions

These are some of the more well known resources, and ones that I know and trust. At least you'll have a place to start for anything you want to know more about. There are many more groups, organizations and businesses dedicated to providing information and support to new and expectant families, and to doulas.

As far as the definitions go, these are the core members of the maternity care support team. There are others who provide very specific support such as herbalists, nutritionists, and chiropractors. And, there are more. Again, you have the starting point, and you can expand from there.

Advocacy Organizations

Childbirth Connection

Formerly the Maternity Care Association, Childbirth Connection has great free downloadable documents to read. They also have a slideshow on your body during pregnancy. This organization has the latest research and best available data about the childbearing year, including a booklet on avoiding cesarean section and the Listening to Mothers Survey. This is a great place to start your search for information.

Improving Birth

Recently three organizations came together: Improving Birth, Birth Network National and the Coalition for Improving Maternity Services.

This organization is focused on advocating for women to take a stand, and to share their birth stories. They highlight the trauma and abuse in the maternity care system, and provide ways for you to find your power.

Improving Birth has an Advocacy Tool Kit, a blog, an annual rally on Labor Day, and chapters around the country working locally to improve birth.

International Cesarean Awareness Network ICAN

1 in 3 women in the United States (higher in some states and hospitals), give birth by cesarean section, major abdominal surgery.

The International Cesarean Awareness Network is a non-profit organization whose mission is to improve maternal-child health by reducing preventable cesareans through education, supporting cesarean recovery, and advocating for vaginal birth after cesarean (VBAC). ICAN has chapters in every state. You can find one near you by going to the website.

If there isn't a chapter near you, then you can start one!

Postpartum Support International (PSI)

This is your go-to for information, support and resources about Perinatal Mood and Anxiety Disorders (PMADs). There are support groups all over the United States, and you can start one if there isn't one in your area. They also have a phone line to chat with an expert.

PSI offers conferences, as well as the Climb Out of Darkness event each year to raise awareness about mood disorders and its effects on women and families.

La Leche League International (LLLI)

This is a world-wide support group and breastfeeding advocacy organization. There are local chapters that provide periodic meetings you can attend before and while you are pregnant to learn more about breastfeeding. You have an opportunity to see breastfeeding Moms and babies, and ask questions.

Great Evidence-Based Information

·

Childbirth U

There is a variety of information on this website about birth, pregnancy, the postpartum period, and optimal care. You will find many free downloads and some free lectures. Other lectures can be purchased for a nominal fee. There is an option for an annual subscription, which is well worth its value.

The website's owner, Henci Goer, is a well-known author, and speaker, and is known for her ability to break down the research in an easy to understand way.

Evidence-Based Birth

This is an online resource for information and inspiration. Many free handouts and articles to read. There are also courses you can take. Evidence Based Birth trains instructors, so you may find one in your area.

This is a great place to go for articles that provide clarification on a particular procedure or intervention. For example, ultrasound. If you are asking if it is appropriate, safe, and medically necessary, this could be a great place to get your answer.

Plus Size Birth

If you are a plus size woman, this is the place for you. All you need to know about being pregnant and plus size. Here you will find a great free guide book, lots of blog articles, and a course for you to delve further.

Jen McLellan was where you are today, and she offers all her wisdom and guidance.

VBAC Education Project

The VBAC Education Project was created by Nicette Jukelevics, to give women access to free information about vaginal birth after cesarean. There are fourteen learning modules, and lots of resources for parents and for birth professionals. The material is easy to read.

This project is endorsed by the International Cesarean Awareness Network and the International Childbirth Education Association.

Childbirth Preparation Methods and Classes

Lamaze

The Lamaze method has changed over the years. They used to be known for particular breathing patterns. Today's focus is on the Six Healthy Birth Practices. It is all about confidence, support and feeling powerful.

The Bradley Method

Bradley method is most known for the husband coached approach. The goal of the course is for you to have a natural birth. It is usually a 12-week course that prepares you for this goal. There is an extensive workbook with lots of illustrations.

HypnoBirthing

This has become a very popular birth preparation method. You will learn and practice breathing, visualization, and meditation. Focus on nutrition is also emphasized. All of these things will help you to relax between contractions and to cope with labor.

You are learning self-hypnosis to rid yourself of the stories of pain and fear you may have heard from other women.

Hypnobabies

Hypnobabies provides tapes with scripts for Moms to practice while pregnant, to retrain their sub-conscious minds. The goal is for the brain to create a new perception about pain.

There is a curriculum to go along with the hypnosis training. Lots of information for you if you are curious to know more about hypnosis, and how it works.

Books and Other Resources (some of my favorites)

Ina May's Guide to Childbirth

This book is packed with stories and information from a well-seasoned midwife. Ina May shares about orgasmic birth, what really happens in labor, and how to avoid unnecessary intervention.

Ancient Map for Modern Birth

This book is by the creator of Birthing From Within, Pam England. It is a very thorough guide for preparing for anything and everything. It ties together the old with the new. The book weaves together your inner spiritual path with your outer path to birth.

Orgasmic Birth

Yes, birth can be orgasmic. It can be filled with pleasure, and be the most amazing experience of a woman's life. The goal is not orgasm, but rather an experience to enjoy, and one where you claim your power. This book shines a light on that possibility.

Ten Questions to Ask

This free downloadable tool was developed by the Coalition for Improving Maternity Services, which is now part of the Improving Birth Coalition. These are important questions to ask your doctor or midwife.

What to Reject When You're Expecting

This is a shortened version of the Consumer Reports publication, and an unbiased look at maternity care in the United States.

Sweet Sleep

This book is for the breastfeeding Mom. It's loaded with strategies to get the rest needed while breastfeeding.

The No Cry Sleep Solution

This book will help you to understand baby's sleep patterns, and how different they are from adults. Once new parents learn to distinguish sleep time from over stimulation time, they'll gain much confidence as a new parent. They'll also get more sleep.

Your Guide to Breastfeeding

This is a great, easy to read, free resource for breastfeeding information. It's published by the Office of Women's Health.

Definition and Descriptions of Birth Team Members

Midwife

The midwife is a trained birth clinician. There are many different types. Some practice in hospitals, and others work at birth centers, or have a homebirth practice. The midwife will care for you during your pregnancy and be there for your birth. She may work with a back-up midwife, who will be there for you if your primary midwife is unable. Homebirth midwives usually visit you once or twice at home after you give birth. Midwives usually practice within the midwifery model of care. This view sees birth as a normal physiological event that requires no or very little intervention.

Obstetrician

The obstetrician (OB) is a trained surgeon, who is most often associated with a hospital. The OB will take care of you prenatally, and may be there for your birth. This depends on whether they are in a solo or group practice. Obstetricians typically practice within the medical model of care. This view sees birth as a crisis waiting to happen, and an event that requires intervention and management.

Birth Doula

A birth doula will be with you during your pregnancy, from the time you hire her, until after your birth. Typically you will meet two or three times before birth to develop your vision and answer questions you might have. Your birth doula will stay with you during labor and birth, and will visit you at least once after birth. Doulas determine their own price and services. There is no diagnosing or prescribing.

Postpartum Doula

A postpartum doula will care for you after you have your baby.

She will tend to your needs, including breastfeeding support, nutrition, and guidance with newborn care and development. Your postpartum doula should have a list of local resources if you need other support. She should be well-versed in normal newborn care, early breastfeeding challenges, and should be aware of the signs and symptoms of any kind of emotional adjustment issue. There is no diagnosing or prescribing.

Certified Lactation Counselor (CLC)

The lactation counselor is a trained breastfeeding professional. She has taken a 40-hour course and an exam, and is able to handle many challenges that may arise with breastfeeding. Some counselors practice in hospitals and doctors' offices.

International Board Certified Lactation Consultant (IBCLC)

The Board-certified lactation consultant has much more extensive training and clinical hours. This is a step above the lactation counselor. Oftentimes, the consultants are present at the hospital as part of the staff. If there is a breastfeeding situation that is beyond the scope of practice or knowledge of the counselor, she will likely refer you to a lactation consultant.

Made in the USA
Las Vegas, NV
10 February 2023